7

Show What You Know® on the
COMMON CORE

Assessing Student Knowledge of the Common Core State Standards (CCSS)

Reading

Name: _____

Published by:

Show What You Know® Publishing
A Division of Englefield & Associates, Inc.
P.O. Box 341348
Columbus, OH 43234-1348
Phone: 614-764-1211
www.showwhatyouknowpublishing.com

Standards are from the Common Core State Standards Initiative website at www.corestandards.org dated 2011.

Printed in the United States of America
13   12   11   20 19 18 17 16 15 14 13 12 11 10 9 8 7 6 5 4 3 2 1

ISBN: 1-59230-462-1

Acknowledgements

Show What You Know® Publishing acknowledges the following for their efforts in making this assessment material available for students, parents, and teachers:

Cindi Englefield, President/Publisher
Eloise Boehm-Sasala, Vice President/Managing Editor
Jennifer Harney, Editor/Illustrator

About the Contributors

The content of this book was written BY teachers FOR teachers and students and was designed specifically for the Common Core State Standards for Grade 7 Reading. Contributions to the Reading section of this book were also made by the educational publishing staff at Show What You Know® Publishing. Dr. Jolie S. Brams, a clinical child and family psychologist, is the contributing author of the Test Anxiety and Test-Taking Strategies chapters of this book. Without the contributions of these people, this book would not be possible.

Table of Contents

Introduction..**v**

Test Anxiety..**1**

Test-Taking Strategies..**11**

Reading...**25**

    Introduction 25

    Glossary of Reading Terms 26

    Reading Assessment One...29

        Directions 29

        Reading Assessment One Answer Document..65

    Reading Assessment Two 69

        Directions 69

        Reading Assessment Two Answer Document...99

Introduction

Dear Student:

This *Show What You Know® on the Common Core for Grade 7 Reading, Student Workbook,* was created to give you lots of practice in preparation for your state proficiency test in Reading.

The first two chapters in this workbook—Test Anxiety and Test-Taking Strategies—were written especially for seventh-grade Reading students. Test Anxiety offers advice on how to get rid of the bad feelings you may have about tests. The Test-Taking Strategies chapter gives you examples of the kinds of questions you will see on the test and includes helpful tips on how to answer these questions correctly so you can succeed on all tests.

The next chapter of this Student Workbook helps you prepare for the Reading test.
- The Reading chapter includes two full-length Reading Assessments and a Glossary of Reading Terms that will help you show what you know.

This Student Workbook will provide a chance to practice your test-taking skills and build your confidence with the Grade 7 Reading Assessment.

Good luck!

This page intentionally left blank.

Test Anxiety

What is Test Anxiety?

Test anxiety is just a fancy name for feeling nervous about tests. Everyone knows what it is like to be nervous. Feeling nervous is not a good experience.

Many students have anxiety about taking tests, so if you are a test worrier, don't let it worry you. Most likely, many of your fellow students and friends also have fearful feelings about tests but do not share these feelings with others. Seventh grade is a time when everyone wants to seem "grown up," and few seventh graders want to look weak or afraid in the eyes of their friends or their teachers. But not talking to others about anxiety only makes the situation worse. It makes you feel alone and also makes you wonder if there is something "wrong" with you. Be brave! Talk to your friends and teachers about test anxiety. You will feel better for sharing.

What Does It Feel Like to Have Test Anxiety?

Students who have test anxiety don't always feel the same way, but they always feel bad. Here are some ways that students feel when they are anxious about tests.

- **Students who have test anxiety rarely think good things about themselves.**
  They lack confidence in their abilities, and they are convinced they will do poorly on tests. Not only do they feel bad about themselves and their abilities, but they just can't keep negative thoughts out of their minds. They would probably make terrible detectives, because in spite of all the good things they could find out about themselves, they only think about what they can't do. And that's not the worst of it. Students with test anxiety also exaggerate. When they think of the smallest problem, it becomes a hundred times bigger, especially when they think about tests. They are very unforgiving of themselves. If they make a mistake, they always think the worst or exaggerate the situation. If they do poorly on a quiz, they never say, "Well, it's just a quiz, and I'll try better next time." Instead they think, "That test was terrible and I can only imagine how badly I'll do next week." For students with test anxiety, there is never a brighter day ahead. They don't think many good thoughts about themselves, and they certainly don't have a happy outlook on their lives.

- **Students who have test anxiety have poor "thinking habits."**
  Negative thinking is a habit just like any other habit. Some habits are good and some habits are bad, but negative thinking is probably the worst habit of all. A habit forms when you do something over and over again until it becomes so much a part of you that you don't think about it anymore. Students with test anxiety get into bad thinking habits. They develop negative ways of thinking about themselves and about schoolwork, especially about tests. They tend to make the worst out of situations and imagine all kinds of possibilities that probably will not happen. Their thoughts grow like a mushroom out of control. Besides having negative ideas about tests, they begin to have negative ideas about almost everything else in their lives. This is not a good way of thinking because the more negative they feel about themselves, the worse they do in school, and bad grades make them feel even worse about themselves. What a mess. Students who have constant negative thoughts about themselves and schoolwork probably have test anxiety.

- **Students who have test anxiety may feel physically uncomfortable or even ill.**
It is important to know that your mind and body are connected. What goes on in your mind can change how your body feels, and how your body feels can influence what goes on in your thinking. When students have test anxiety, their thoughts might cause them to have physical symptoms which include a fast heartbeat, butterflies in the stomach, headaches, and all sorts of other physical problems. Some kids become so ill they end up going to the doctor because they believe they are truly sick. Some students miss a lot of school due to anxiety, but they aren't really ill. Instead, their thoughts are controlling their bodies in a negative way. Some anxious students do not realize that what they are feeling is anxiety. They miss many days of school, not because they are lazy or neglectful, but because they believe they truly are not feeling well. Unfortunately, the more school they miss, the more behind they are and the more nervous they feel. Students who suffer from test anxiety probably feel even worse on test days. Their uncomfortable physical feelings will make them either avoid the test completely or feel so bad during the test that they do poorly. Guess what happens then. They feel even worse about themselves, become more anxious, and the cycle goes on and on.

- **Students who have test anxiety "freak out" and want to escape.**
Many students feel so bad when they are anxious that they will do anything to avoid that feeling. For most students, this means running away from problems, especially tests. Some students try to get away from tests by missing school. This does not solve any problems; the more a student is away from school, the harder schoolwork is, and the worse he or she feels. Some students worry about being worried. It may sound silly, but they are worried that they are going to freak out, and guess what happens . . . they do. They are so terrified that they will have uncontrollable anxious feelings that they actually get anxious feelings when thinking about this problem. For many students, anxiety is such a bad feeling that they will do anything not to feel anxious, even if it means failing tests or school. Although they know this will cause them problems in the future, their anxiety is so overwhelming they would rather avoid anxiety now and fail later. Unfortunately, this is usually what happens.

- **Students who have test anxiety do not show what they know on tests.**
Students who have test anxiety do not make good decisions on tests. Instead of focusing their thoughts, planning out their answers, and using what they know, students find themselves "blanking out." They stare at the paper, and no answer is there. They become "stuck" and cannot move on. Some students come up with the wrong answers because their anxiety gets in the way of reading directions carefully and thinking about answers thoughtfully. Their minds are running in a hundred different ways and none of those ways seem to be getting them anywhere. They forget to use what they know, and they also forget to use study skills that can help students do their best. When students are so worried that they cannot make good decisions and use all of the talents they have, it is called test anxiety.

Are You One of These "Test-Anxious" Seventh Graders?

As you have seen, students with test anxiety have negative thoughts about themselves, often feel anxious to the point of being ill, freak out and want to escape, and rarely show what they know on tests. Do any of the following kids remind you of yourself?

Stay-Away Stephanie

Stephanie's thoughts tell her it is better to stay away from challenges, especially tests. Stephanie is a good girl, but she is always in trouble at school for avoiding tests. Sometimes, she really feels ill and begs her mom to allow her to stay home on test days. At other times, Stephanie does anything to avoid school, refusing to get up in the morning or to leave the house to catch the bus. Stephanie truly believes there is nothing worse than taking a test. She is so overwhelmed with anxiety that she forgets about the problems that will happen when she stays away from her responsibilities. Unfortunately, the more she stays away, the worse the situation becomes. Stay-Away Stephanie feels less nervous when she doesn't face a test, but she never learns to face her fears.

Worried Wendy

Wendy is the type of seventh grader who always expects the worst thing to happen. She has many negative thoughts. Even when situations have turned out to be OK, Wendy focuses on the few bad things that happened. She exaggerates negative events and forgets about everything good. Her mind races a mile a

minute with all sorts of thoughts and ideas about tests. The more she thinks, the worse she feels, and her problems become unbelievably huge. Instead of just worrying about a couple of difficult questions on a test, she finds herself thinking about failing the whole test, being made fun of by her friends, being grounded by her parents, and never going to college. She completely forgets that her parents would never be so strict, that her friends like her for many more reasons than her test grades, and that she has all sorts of career choices ahead of her. No one is going to hold it against her if she performed poorly on a test. It is not going to ruin her life. However, Wendy believes all of that would happen. Her negative thoughts get in the way of thinking anything positive.

Critical Chris

Chris is the type of seventh grader who spends all of his time putting himself down. No matter what happens, he always feels he has been a failure. While some people hold grudges against others, Chris holds grudges against himself. No matter what little mistakes he makes, he can never forget them. Chris has had many good things happen to him in his life, and he has been successful many times. Unfortunately, Chris forgets all the good and only remembers the bad. Because he doesn't appreciate himself, Chris has test anxiety.

Victim Vince

Most seventh graders find it is important to take responsibility for their actions. It helps them understand that adulthood is just around the corner, and that they are smarter and more able than they ever thought  they were. However, Vince is not like this. He can't take responsibility for himself at all. He thinks everything is someone else's fault and constantly complains about friends, parents, schoolwork, and especially tests. He tells himself, "They make those tests too hard." He sees the teachers as unfair, and he thinks life is generally against him. Vince does not feel there is anything he can do to help his situation, and there is little he thinks he can do to help himself with tests. Because he does not try to learn test-taking skills or to understand why he is afraid, he continues to feel hopeless and angry. Not surprisingly, he does poorly on tests, which only makes his thoughts about the world around him worse.

Perfect Pat

Everyone knows that there is more homework and responsibility in seventh grade than in previous grades. Everyone in the seventh grade needs to try his or her best, but no one should try as much as Pat does. All Pat does is worry. No matter what she does, it's never good enough. She will write book reports over and over and study for  tests until she is exhausted. Trying hard is fine, but no matter what Pat does, she feels she has never done enough. Because she never accomplishes what she sets out to do (that would be impossible.), she worries all the time. Her anxiety level gets higher and higher. The more anxious she becomes, the worse she does on tests. This just makes her study and worry more. What a terrible situation!

How Do I Handle Test Anxiety?

Test anxiety is a very powerful feeling that convinces students they are weak and helpless. Feelings of test anxiety can be so powerful it seems there is nothing you can do to stop them. Anxiety seems to take over your mind and body and leaves you feeling like you are going to lose the test anxiety battle for sure.

The good news is that there are many simple things you can do to win the battle over test anxiety. If you can learn these skills in the seventh grade, you are on the road to success in school and for all other challenges in your life.

- **Change the way you think.**
  Most of us don't "think about how we think." We just go along thinking our thoughts and never really consider whether they are helpful or not helpful or if they are right or wrong. We rarely realize how much the way we think has to do with how well we get along in life. Our thoughts can influence how we feel about ourselves, how we get along with other people, how well we do in school, and how we perform on tests.

- **The Soda Pop Test.**
  Most seventh graders have heard a parent or teacher tell them, "There is more than one side to any story." One student reported that his grandfather used to say, "There's more than one way to paint a fence." Have you ever considered how you think about different situations? Most situations can be looked at in many ways, both good and bad.

  Take a can of soda pop and put it on your desk or dresser at home. Get out a piece of paper and a pen or a pencil. Now, draw a line down the middle of the paper. On one side, put a heading: "All the bad things about this can of soda pop." On the other side put another heading: "All the good things about this can of soda pop." If you think about that can of soda pop, you might come up with the following chart.

All the bad things about this can of soda pop	All the good things about this can of soda pop
Not an attractive color	Easy-to-read lettering
It's getting warm	Nice to have something to drink
Not much in the can	Inexpensive
Has a lot of sugar	Recyclable aluminum cans

Look how easy it is to write down good things or bad things about a silly can of soda pop. That can of soda pop is not really good or bad, it's just a can of soda pop, but we can either look at it in a positive way or we can think about everything negative that comes to our minds. Doesn't the same thing hold true for tests? Tests are not good or bad in themselves. Tests are just a way to challenge us and see what we know. Challenges can be stressful, but they can also be rewarding. Studying for tests can be boring and can take up a lot of free time, but we can also learn a lot and feel great about ourselves when we study. The way you think about tests will help determine how you do in a test-taking situation. Most importantly, how you feel about tests is related to your level of anxiety about test taking. Students who have negative thoughts and feelings about tests become anxious. Students who think positively are less anxious. To reduce test anxiety, try thinking about tests and testing situations using a positive frame of mind.

- **All or Nothing Thinking.**
  Nothing is ever as simple as it seems. Sometimes we convince ourselves something is going to be "awful" or "wonderful." Rarely does it turn out that way.

  Trouble comes along when students think tests are going to be an "awful" experience. If you dread something happening, it is only going to make things worse. Also, you may be wrong. Nothing is as terrible as it seems. All the negative thoughts you have about the upcoming test cannot possibly be true. Thinking something is "awful" or "terrible" and nothing else only leads to trouble and failure. The more negative you feel about something, the worse things turn out.

  Very few things are "all good" or "all bad." This is especially true for tests. Recognizing the "bad" parts of tests can help you be successful. For example, the fact that you need to study for tests, to pay attention while you are taking tests, and to understand there are probably many more fun things to do in school than take tests are all "true" thoughts. "Good" thoughts are just as true, including the good feelings one gets from studying and the chance that you might do well. Having "all or nothing" thinking is going to get you nowhere. Successful and happy students know some experiences are better than others, but they try to look at a situation from all sides.

- **Mind Reading.**
  Some students believe they can read the minds of their parents and teachers. They assume if they do poorly on a test, everyone will think they are "dumb" or "lazy." The more their minds create all the terrible things that people may say about them, the more anxious they get. This just increases anxiety and definitely does not help students do well on tests.

- **Catastrophizing.**

When people catastrophize, they make everything a catastrophe. A catastrophe is a disaster. It is when something terrible happens. When a student catastrophizes, his or her mind goes on and on creating terrible scenes of disasters. If someone put all these ideas into a movie script, the writer might be rich.

Your state proficiency test is an important part of a seventh-grader's school year. It is a test that helps the student, the teacher, and the school. However, a seventh-grade student is much more than just his or her score on the test. Each student is an individual who has his or her own great personality, talents, and other successes in school. If what people catastrophized about was really true, the whole world would be a terrible mess. Imagine if your mother cooked a dinner that didn't turn out quite right. This might mean everyone has to go out for fast food, but you wouldn't love your mother any less. It would be catastrophizing if your mother said, "Now that I burned the dinner, none of my kids will love me. They will probably just want to move out as quickly as they can, and my life will be ruined." Catastrophizing about a test is just as bad. Thinking that this test is going to be the worst experience of your life and that your future will be ruined will not help you feel comfortable when preparing for and taking the test.

- **Making "Should" Statements.**

Students make themselves anxious when they think they "should" do everything. They feel they "should" be as smart as everyone else, "should" study more, and "should" not feel anxious about tests. All these thoughts are pretty ridiculous. You can't always be as smart as the next person, and you do not have to study until you drop to do well on tests. Instead of kicking yourself for not being perfect, it is better to think about all the good things you have done in your life. This will help you do better on tests and be happier in your life by reducing your anxiety.

How Do I Replace Worried Thoughts with Positive Ones?

As we have learned, there are all kinds of thoughts that make us anxious, such as feeling we "should" do everything, thinking we can read peoples' minds, catastrophizing, and thinking only bad thoughts about a situation. Learning how to stop these types of thoughts is very important. Understanding your thoughts and doing something about them help control test anxiety.

People who are worried or anxious can become happier when thinking positive thoughts. Even when situations are scary, such as a visit to the dentist, "positive imagery" is helpful. "Positive imagery" means thinking good thoughts to keep from thinking anxious thoughts. Positive and negative thoughts do not go together. If you are thinking something positive, it is almost impossible to think of something negative. Keep this in mind when test anxiety starts to become a bother.

Try these ideas the next time you find yourself becoming anxious.

- **Thoughts of Success.**
  Thinking "I can do it" thoughts can chase away thoughts of failure. Imagine times you were successful, such as when you performed well in a dance recital or figured out a complicated brain teaser. These are good things to think about. Telling yourself you have been successful in the past and can be successful in the future will chase away thoughts of anxiety.

- **Relaxing Thoughts.**
  Some people find that thinking calming or relaxing thoughts is helpful. Picturing a time in which you felt comfortable and happy can lessen your anxious feelings. Imagine yourself playing a baseball game, running through a park, or eating an ice cream cone; these are all positive thoughts that may get in the way of anxious ones. Some students find that listening to music on the morning of a test is helpful. It probably doesn't matter what music you listen to, as long as it makes you feel good about yourself, confident, and relaxed.

  Just as you can calm your mind, it is also important for you to relax your body. Practice relaxing your body. When students have test anxiety, their muscles become stiff. In fact, the whole body becomes tense. Taking deep breaths before a test and letting them out slowly as well as relaxing muscles in your body are all very helpful ways to feel less anxious. Your school counselors will probably have more ideas about relaxation. You may find that relaxation doesn't just help you on tests, but is helpful for other challenging situations and for feeling healthy overall.

- **Don't Let Yourself Feel Alone.**
  Everyone feels more anxious when they feel alone and separate from others. Talking to your friends, parents, and teachers about your feelings helps. Feeling anxious about tests does not mean there is something wrong with you. You will be surprised to find that many of your friends and fellow students also feel anxious about tests. You may be even more surprised to learn your parents and teachers have also had test anxiety. They know what you are going through and are there to support you.

- **Take Care of Yourself.**
  Everyone is busy. Many seventh graders are involved in all sorts of activities, including sports, music, and helping around the house. Often, you are so busy you forget to eat breakfast or you don't get enough sleep. Eating and sleeping right are important, especially before a test like your state proficiency test. If you are not a big breakfast eater, try to find something that you like to eat and get in the habit of eating breakfast. When you do not eat right, you may feel shaky and have a hard time concentrating, and your anxiety can increase. Being tired does not help either. Try to get in the habit of going to bed at a good time every night (especially the night before a test) so you can feel fresh, rested, and confident.

- **Practice Your Test-Taking Success.**
  People who have accomplished incredibly difficult goals have used their imaginations to help them achieve success. They thought about what they would do step by step to be successful.

  You can do the same. Think about yourself on the morning of the test. Imagine telling yourself positive thoughts and eating a good breakfast. Think about arriving at school and feeling confident that you will do fine on the test. Imagine closing your eyes before the test, breathing deeply, relaxing, and remembering all the study skills you have learned. The more you program your mind to think in a successful and positive way, the better off you will be.

- **Learn to Use Study Skills.**
  The next chapter in this book will help you learn test-taking strategies. The more you know about taking tests successfully, the calmer you will feel. Knowledge is power. Practice test-taking strategies to reduce your test anxiety.

- **Congratulate Yourself During the Test.**
  Instead of thinking, "I've only done five problems and I've got eight pages to go," or "I knew three answers were right but one mixed me up," reward yourself for what you have done. Tell yourself, "I got some answers right so far, so I bet I can do more." After all, if you don't compliment yourself, who will?

Conclusion

You are not alone if you feel stressed about tests. It is probably good to feel a little anxious, because it motivates you to do well. However, if you feel very anxious about tests, then reading, re-reading, and practicing the suggestions in this chapter will help you "tackle your test anxiety."

Test-Taking Strategies

All Students Can Do Their Best on Tests!

Most students want to do their best on tests. Tests are one important way for teachers to know how well students are doing and for students to understand how much progress they are making in their studies. Tests, like your state proficiency test, help schools measure how well students are learning so teachers and principals can make their schools even better. Students can do the best job possible in "showing what they know" by learning how to be good test takers.

It's just not possible to do a good job without the right tools. Test-taking strategies are tools to help you perform well on tests. Everyone needs good tools and strategies when facing a problem. If you do not have these, even the smartest or most talented person will do poorly. Think about people who are "wizards" at fixing cars and trucks. Your family's car "dies" in the middle of the road. The situation looks pretty hopeless. How are you ever going to get to that basketball game tomorrow if your parent's car is a mechanical mess? Suddenly, "magic" happens. The mechanic at the repair shop calls your parents and tells them the car is ready, just a day after it broke down. How did this happen? It happened because the auto-repair mechanic had a great deal of knowledge about cars. Most importantly, he had the right tools and strategies to fix the car. He knew how to look at the problem, and when he figured out what to do, he had some special gadgets to get the job done. You also can find special ways that will help you be a successful test taker.

Tools You Can Use on Tests Throughout Your Life!

Be An "Active Learner."

You can't learn anything by being a "sponge." Just because you are sitting in a pool of learning (your classroom) does not mean you are going to learn anything just by being there. Instead, students learn when they actively think and participate during the school day. Students who are active learners pay attention to what is being said. They also constantly ask themselves and their teachers questions about the subject. When able, they participate by making comments and joining discussions. Active learners enjoy school, learn more, feel good about themselves, and usually do better on tests. Remember the auto-repair mechanic? That person had a lot of knowledge about fixing cars. All the tools and strategies in the world will not help unless you have benefited from what your teachers have tried to share.

Being an active learner takes time and practice. If you are the type of student who is easily bored or frustrated, it is going to take some practice to use your classroom time differently. Ask yourself the following questions.

- Am I looking at the teacher?

- Do I pay attention to what is being said?

- Do I have any questions or ideas about what the teacher is saying?

- Do I listen to what my fellow students are saying and think about their ideas?

- Do I work with others to try to solve difficult problems?

- Do I look at the clock and wonder what time school will be over, or do I appreciate what is happening during the school day and how much I can learn?

- Do I try to think about how my schoolwork might be helpful to me now or in the future?

Although you do need special tools and strategies to do well on tests, the more you learn, the better chance you have of doing well on tests. Think about Kristen.

There was a young girl named Kristen,
Who was bored and wouldn't listen.
She didn't train
To use her smart brain
And never knew what she was missing!

Don't Depend on Luck.

Preparing for your state proficiency test might feel stressful or boring at times, but it is an important part of learning how to show what you know and doing your best. Even the smartest student needs to spend time taking practice tests and listening to the advice of teachers about how to do well. Luck alone is not going to help you do well on tests. People who depend on luck do not take responsibility for themselves. Some people who believe in luck do not want to take the time and effort to do well. It is easier for them to say, "It's not my fault I did poorly. It's just not my lucky day." Some people just do not feel very good about their abilities. They get in the habit of saying, "Whatever happens will happen." They believe they can never do well no matter how much they practice or prepare. Students who feel they have no control over what happens to them usually have poor grades and do not feel very good about themselves.

Your performance on tests is not going to be controlled by luck. Instead, you can have a lot of control over how well you do in many areas of your life, including test taking. Don't be like Chuck.

There was a cool boy named Chuck,
Who thought taking tests was just luck.
He never prepared.
He said, "I'm not scared."
When his test scores appear, he should duck!

Do Your Best Every Day.

Many students find seventh grade much different than other grades. Suddenly, the work seems really hard. Not only that, but your teachers are no longer treating you like a baby. That's good in some ways, because it gives you more freedom and responsibility, but there sure is a lot to learn. You might feel the same way about tests; you may feel you'll never be prepared. Many times when we are faced with new challenges, it is easy just to give up.

Students are surprised when they find that if they just set small goals for themselves, they can learn an amazing amount. If you learn just one new fact every day of the year, at the end of the year, you will know 365 new facts. You could use those to impress your friends and family. Now think about what would happen if you learned three new facts every day. At the end of the year, you would have learned 1,095 new facts. Soon you will be on your way to having a mind like an encyclopedia.

When you think about a test or any other academic challenge, try to focus on what you can learn step by step and day by day. You will be surprised how all of this learning adds up to make you one of the smartest seventh graders ever. Think about Ray.

There was a smart boy named Ray,
Who learned something new every day.
He was pretty impressed
With what his mind could possess.
His excellent scores were his pay!

Get to Know the Test.
Most seventh graders are probably pretty used to riding in their parents' cars. They know how to make the air-conditioning cooler or warmer, how to change the radio stations, and how to adjust the volume on the radio. Think about being a passenger in a totally unfamiliar car. You might think, "What are all those buttons? How do I even turn on the air conditioner? How do I make the window go up and down?" Now, think about taking your state proficiency test. Your state proficiency test is a test, but it may be different than some tests you have taken in the past. The more familiar you are with the types of questions on the test and how to record your answers, the better you will do. Working through the reading chapters in this book will help you get to know the test. Becoming familiar with the test is a great test-taking tool. Think about Sue.

There was a kid named Sue,
Who thought her test looked new.
"I never saw this before!
How'd I get a bad score?"
If she practiced, she might have a clue!

Read Directions and Questions Carefully!

One of the worst mistakes a student can make on a test is to ignore directions or to read questions carelessly. By the time some students are in the seventh grade, they think they have heard every direction or question ever invented, and it is easy for them to "tune out" directions. Telling yourself, "These directions are just like other directions," or "I'm not really going to take time to read this question because I know what the question will be," are not good test-taking strategies. It is impossible to do well on any test without knowing what is being asked.

Reading directions and questions slowly, repeating them to yourself, and asking yourself if what you are reading makes sense are powerful test-taking strategies. Think about Fred.

There was a nice boy named Fred,
Who ignored almost all that he read.
The directions were easy,
But he said, "I don't need these!"
He should have read them instead.

Know How to Fill in Those Answer Bubbles!

Most seventh graders have taken tests that ask them to fill in answer bubbles. You might be a very bright seventh grader, but you will never "show what you know" unless you fill in the answer bubbles correctly. Don't forget: a computer will be "reading" your multiple-choice question answers. If you do not fill in the answer bubble darkly or if you use a check mark or dot instead of a dark mark, your smart thinking will not be counted. Look at the examples given below.

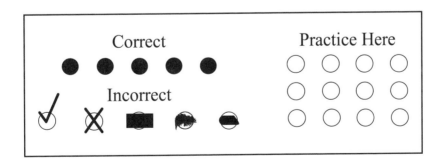

Learning how to fill in answer bubbles takes practice, practice, and more practice. It may not be how you are used to answering multiple-choice questions, but it is the only way to give a right answer on your state proficiency test. Think about Kay!

A stubborn girl named Kay,
Liked to answer questions her own way.
So her marked answer bubbles,
Gave her all sorts of troubles.
Her test scores ruined her day!

Speeding Through the Test Doesn't Help.

Most students have more than enough time to read and answer all the questions on a test. There will always be some students who finish the test more quickly than others, but this does not mean the test was easier for them or their answers are correct. Whether you finish at a faster rate or at a slower rate than other students in your class is not important. As long as you take your time, are well prepared, concentrate on the test, and use some of the skills in this book, you should be able to do just fine. You will not get a better score just because you finish the test before everyone else. Speeding through a test item or through a whole test does not help you do well. In fact, students do their best when they work at a medium rate of speed, not too slow and not too fast. Students who work too slowly tend to get worried about their answers and sometimes change correct answers into incorrect ones. Students who work too fast often make careless mistakes, and many of them do not read directions or questions carefully. Think about Liz.

There was a eighth grader named Liz,
Who sped through her test like a whiz.
She thought she should race
At a very fast pace,
But it caused her to mess up her quiz.

Answer Every Question.

There is no reason that you should not attempt to answer every question you encounter on a test. Even if you don't know the answer, there are ways for you to increase your chances of choosing the correct response. Use the helpful strategies described below to help you answer every question to the best of your ability.

- **If you don't know the answer, guess.**

  Did you know that on your state proficiency there is no penalty for guessing? That is really good news. That means you have a one out of four chance of getting a multiple-choice question right, even if you just close your eyes and guess. That means that for every four questions you guess, you should get about 25% (1 out of 4) of the questions right. Guessing alone is not going to make you a star on the test, but leaving multiple-choice items blank is not going to help you either.

  Now comes the exciting part. If you can rule out one of the four answer choices, your chances of answering correctly are now one out of three. You can almost see your test score improving right before your eyes.

  Although it is always better to be prepared for the test and to study in school, we all have to guess at one time or another. Some of us do not like to guess because we are afraid of choosing the wrong answer, but on a test, it is better to guess than leave an answer blank. Think about Jess.

There was a smart girl named Jess,
Who thought it was useless to guess.
If a question was tough,
She just gave up.
This only added to her stress.

- **Use a "code" to help you make good guesses.**

  Some students use a "code" to rate each answer when they feel they might have to guess. Using your pencil in the test booklet, you can mark the following codes next to each multiple-choice response so you can make the best possible guess. The codes are as follows:

(+) Putting a "plus sign" by your answer means you are not sure if this answer is correct, but you think this answer is probably more correct than the others.

(?) Putting a "question mark" by your answer means you are unsure if this is the correct answer, but you don't want to rule it out completely.

(–) Putting a "minus sign" by your answer means you are pretty sure this is the wrong answer. You should then choose from the other answers to make an educated guess.

Remember, it is fine to write in your test booklet. Think about Dwight.

There was a smart kid named Dwight,
Who marked answers that looked to be right.
He'd put a plus sign
Or a dash or a line.
Now the whole world knows he is bright!

- **Use what you know to "power guess."**
  Not everything you know was learned in a classroom. Part of what you know comes from just living your life. When you take a test, you should use everything you have learned in school, but you should also use your experiences outside the classroom to help you answer questions correctly. Using your "common sense," as well as other information you know, will help you do especially well on a test. Try to use what you know from the world around you to eliminate obviously wrong answers. If you can rule out just one answer that you are certain is not correct, you are going to greatly increase your chances of guessing another answer correctly. For example, if you are given a question in which you are asked the definition of a word, and one of the answers reminds you of something you saw on TV, you might be able to count that answer out using your own experiences. Although the reading might be difficult for you, your common sense has eliminated one likely wrong answer. Think about Drew.

There was a boy named Drew,
Who forgot to use what he knew.
He had lots of knowledge.
He could have been in college!
But his right answers were few.

• **Do Not Get Stuck on One Question.**

One of the worst things you can do on a test is to get stuck on one question. Your state proficiency test gives you many chances to show all that you have learned. Not knowing the answer to one or two questions is not going to hurt your test results very much.

When you become stuck on a question, your mind plays tricks on you. You begin to think that you are a total failure, and your worries become greater and greater. This worrying gets in the way of your doing well on the rest of the test. Remember, very few students know all the answers on a test. If you are not sure of the answer after spending some time on it, mark it in your test booklet and come back to it later. When you come back to that question later, you might find a new way of thinking. Sometimes, another question or answer later in the test will remind you of a possible answer to the question that had seemed difficult. If not, you can use your guessing strategies to solve the questions you are unsure of after you have answered all the questions you know. Also, when you move on from a troubling question and find you are able to answer other questions correctly, you will feel much better about yourself and you will feel calmer. This will help you have a better chance of succeeding on a question that made you feel "stuck." Think about Von.

There was a sweet girl named Von,
Who got stuck and just couldn't go on.
She'd sit there and stare,
But the answer wasn't there.
Before she knew it, all the time was gone.

- **Always, and This Means Always, Recheck Your Work.**
Everyone makes mistakes. People make the most mistakes when they feel a little worried or rushed. Checking your work is a very important part of doing your best. This is particularly true in the reading section, where careless mistakes can lead to a wrong answer. Going back and rechecking your answers is very important. You can read a paragraph over again if there is something you do not understand or something that you forgot. If an answer does not seem to make sense, go back and reread the question. Think about Jen.

There was a quick girl named Jen,
Who read stuff once and never again.
It would have been nice
If she'd reread it twice.
Her test scores would be better then!

- **Pay Attention to Yourself and Not Others.**
It is easy to look around the room and wonder how friends are doing. However, it is important to think about how you are using tools and strategies. Don't become distracted by friends. You are going to waste a lot of time if you try to figure out what your friends are doing. Instead, use that time to "show what you know."

If it becomes hard for you to pay attention, give yourself a little break. If you feel you are getting a little tense or worried, or if a question seems tough, close your eyes for a second or two. Think positive thoughts. Try to put negative thoughts out of your mind. You might want to stretch your arms or feet or move around a little to help you focus. Anything you may do to help pay better attention to the test is a great test-taking strategy. Think about Kirk.

There was a boy named Kirk,
Who thought of everything but his work.
He stared into the air
And squirmed in his chair.
When his test scores come, he won't look!

General Test-Taking Strategies for Reading

There are multiple-choice and short-answer questions on the Reading Assessment in this workbook. Here are some good strategies to use on the Reading Assessment.

- **Read the Question Carefully.**

  It may help to look over the questions before you read through the passage. As you read the passage, look for information that may help you answer the questions.

- **Look for Keywords.**

  Remember, you can write in your test booklet. As you read through the different passages, circle or underline important words you come across. Make notes in the margin with ideas that seem to answer the question.

- **Review What You Read to Find More Details.**

  If you don't think you can answer the question, reread the passage and look for more details.

- **Ask Yourself, "Did I Answer the Question?"**

  Read the answer choice you think is correct to make sure you have answered the question correctly.

- **Circle the Numbers of the Questions You Cannot Answer.**

  If you are not sure of the correct answer, circle the question number and return to it later in the test.

- **Do Not Immediately Pick Your First Answer.**

  Your first choice could be the correct choice, but it could also be a wrong answer that a test maker used to distract you. Recheck your answers.

Specific Strategies for Online Tests

Kids usually have two different kinds of thoughts about taking a test on a computer. Some say, "Well, I use my computer all the time … I'm not going to even pay attention to the test … computers are easy!" Some kids think in the opposite way. They say, "A computer test? That has to be even scarier than a regular test … there is no way I am going to do well!" The truth is that both of them are wrong. You have to use some special strategies to do your best on computer tests, and when you do, you will do your best!

1. **Read the Directions.** Here is a silly question: Would you want to eat a cake your friend made if he didn't read the directions on the box? Probably not! But even if you aren't a famous cook, you could make a pretty good cake if you read and follow directions. If you read the directions for EACH QUESTION you will have a much better chance of showing what you know. Because even if you know a lot, you have to answer what the question asks. Don't leave out this important step to test success!

2. **Don't Go With the First Answer.** Take a little time and read the WHOLE question and ALL the answer choices. The first answer that looks right is not always the best. Think about going out to dinner with your grandmother. You look at the menu and see "Big Ole Burger"! That sounds good. But if you looked at ALL the menu choices, you might have found your favorite tacos! The burger was good, but if you took more time, you would have found a better choice.

3. **Ask Yourself … How Much Time Do I Have?** You will have a certain amount of time to complete each section of the test. Always check to see how much time you will have. Practice also helps. Did you know that football players practice and practice to see how long it takes to line up and start a play? After a while they are more relaxed and don't worry about time running out. You need to take some practice tests to feel comfortable with timed tests.

4. **Is There a Good Way to Guess?** Most of the time it is a good idea to guess, especially if you can make an "educated" guess! That means you know some things about the question, but not everything. Remember to use your common sense, as well as other information you know, to help you make an "educated guess."

5. **When Should You Guess?** Unless the directions say that you will lose points for guessing, go for it! Educated guesses are the best, but even if you are really unsure of the answer, calm down and take a guess. If you have four possible answers, and make a guess, you have a one out of four chance of guessing correctly. That is like having three old pennies and one new penny in a bowl. If you just reach in, you will get the new penny one out of every four times you try. That's why you should answer every question!

6. **Don't Mess With That Test Window!** When people get a little nervous, they tend to make silly mistakes. One kid was rushing to make some toast before running off to school, and he unplugged the toaster instead of making the toast! Figure out how the computer screen works, and DON'T close that test window!

7. **Have a Good Attitude!** The better you feel, the better you will do! Remind yourself of how much you have learned in school. Remember that while this test is important, that your teachers will still like you a lot no matter how you do. Just do your best and feel good about yourself. Did you know that when runners have a good attitude, that they win more often? Well, the same goes for you and tests!

8. **If You Have Time Left, Use it!** You can use extra time to help you do your best! If your computer test allows, review your answers, especially if you guessed at a question or two. Take a deep breath and calm down. You might find that a better answer comes into your mind. Talk to yourself a little about some of your answers. You might ask yourself, "I chose the answer that said that it will take 6 hours for that ice cube to melt. That seems like a long time … maybe I better recheck this and see if that makes sense."

Seventh graders all over have good ideas about tests. Here are some of them!

- Ask yourself, "Did I answer the question that was asked?" Carefully read the question so you can give the right answer.

- Read each answer choice before filling in an answer bubble. Sometimes, you read the first choice, and it seems right. But, when you get to the third choice, you realize that's the correct answer. If you had stopped with the first choice, you would have answered the question incorrectly. It is important to read all four choices before answering the question.

- Remember, nobody is trying to trick you. Do not look for trick answers. There will always be a right answer. If the answer choices do not look right, mark the question and go back to it later.

- Don't look around the room. Don't worry about how fast your friends are working, and don't worry about how well they are doing. Only worry about yourself. If you do that, you will do better on the test.

Reading

Introduction

In the Reading section of the *Show What You Know® on the Common Core for Grade 7 Reading, Student Workbook*, you will be asked questions to test what you have learned so far in school. These questions are based on the reading skills you have been taught in school through the seventh grade. The questions you will answer are not meant to confuse or trick you but are written so you have the best chance to show what you know.

The *Show What You Know® on the Common Core for Grade 7 Reading, Student Workbook,* includes two full-length Reading Assessments that will help you practice your test-taking skills.

Glossary

alliteration: Repeating the same sound at the beginning of several words in a phrase or sentence. For example, "The bees buzzed in the back of the blue barn."

adjectives: Words that describe nouns.

adverbs: Words that describe verbs.

antonyms: Words that mean the opposite (e.g., *light* is an antonym of *dark*).

audience: The people who read a written piece or hear the piece being read.

author's purpose: The reason an author writes, such as to entertain, to inform, or to persuade.

author's tone: The attitude the writer takes toward an audience, a subject, or a character. Tone is shown through the writer's choice of words and details. Examples of tone are happy, sad, angry, gentle, etc.

base word (also called root word): The central part of a word that other word parts may be attached to.

biography: A true story about a person's life.

cause: The reason for an action, feeling, or response.

character: A person or an animal in a story, play, or other literary work.

compare: To use examples to show how things are alike.

contrast: To use examples to show how things are different.

details: Many small parts which help to tell a story.

descriptive text: To create a clear picture of a person, place, thing, or idea by using vivid words.

directions: An order or instructions on how to do something or how to act.

draw conclusion: To make a decision or form an opinion after considering the facts from the text.

effect: A result of a cause.

events: Things that happen.

fact: An actual happening or truth.

fiction: A passage that is made up rather than factually true. Examples of fiction are novels and short stories.

format: The way a published piece of writing looks, including the font, legibility, spacing, margins, and white space.

generalize: To come to a broad idea or rule about something after considering particular facts.

genres: Categories of literary and informational works (e.g., biography, mystery, historical fiction, poetry).

graphic organizer: Any illustration, chart, table, diagram, map, etc., used to help interpret information about the text.

heading: A word or group of words at the top or front of a piece of writing.

infer: To make a guess based on facts and observations.

inference: An important idea or conclusion drawn from reasoning rather than directly stated in the text.

inform: To give knowledge; to tell.

informational text (also called expository text): Text with the purpose of telling about details, facts, and information that is true (nonfiction). Informational text is found in textbooks, encyclopedias, biographies, and newspaper articles.

literary devices: Techniques used to convey an author's message or voice (e.g., figurative language, simile, metaphors, etc.).

literary text (also called narrative text): Text that describes actions or events, usually written as fiction. Examples are novels and short stories.

main idea: The main reason the passage was written; every passage has a main idea. Usually you can find the main idea in the topic sentence of the paragraph.

metaphor: A comparison between two unlike things without using the words "like" or "as." An example of a metaphor is, "My bedroom is a junkyard!"

Copying is Prohibited   © Englefield & Associates, Inc.

Glossary

mood: The feeling or emotion the reader gets from a piece of writing.

nonfiction: A passage of writing that tells about real people, events, and places without changing any facts. Examples of nonfiction are an autobiography, a biography, an essay, a newspaper article, a magazine article, a personal diary, and a letter.

onomatopoeia: The use of words in which the sound of the word suggests the sound associated with it. For example, buzz, hiss, splat.

opinion: What one thinks about something or somebody; an opinion is not necessarily based on facts. Feelings and experiences usually help a person form an opinion.

passage: A passage or writing that may be fiction (literary/narrative) or nonfiction (informational/expository).

persuade: To cause to do something by using reason or argument; to cause to believe something.

plan: A method of doing something that has been thought out ahead of time.

plot: A series of events that make up a story. Plot tells "what happens" in a story, novel, or narrative poem.

plot sequence: The order of events in a story.

poetry: A type of writing that uses images and patterns to express feelings.

point of view: The way a story is told; it could be in first person, omniscient, or in third person.

predict: The ability of the reader to know or expect that something is going to happen in a text before it does.

prefix: A group of letters added to the beginning of a word. For example, *un*tie, *re*build, *pre*teen.

preposition: A word that links another word or group of words to other parts of the sentence. Examples are in, on, of, at, by, between, outside, etc.

problem: An issue or question in a text that needs to be answered.

published work: The final writing draft shared with the audience.

reliable: Sources used for writing that are trustworthy.

resource: A source of help or support.

rhyme: When words have the same last sound. For example, hat/cat, most/toast, ball/call.

root word (also called base word): The central part of a word that other word parts may be attached to.

schema: The accumulated knowledge that a person can draw from life experiences to help understand concepts, roles, emotions, and events.

sentence: A group of words that express a complete thought. It has a subject and a verb.

sequential order: The arrangement or ordering of information, content, or ideas (e.g., a story told in chronological order describes what happened first, then second, then third, etc.).

setting: The time and place of a story or play. The setting helps to create the mood in a story, such as inside a spooky house or inside a shopping mall during the holidays.

simile: A comparison between two unlike things, using the words "like" or "as." "Her eyes are as big as saucers" is an example of a simile.

solution: An answer to a problem.

stanzas: Lines of poetry grouped together.

story: An account of something that happened.

story elements: The important parts of the story, including characters, setting, plot, problem, and solution.

style: A way of writing that is individual to the writer, such as the writer's choice of words, phrases, and images.

suffix: A group of letters added to the end of a word. For example, teach*er*, color*ful*, sugar*less*, etc.

summary: To retell what happens in a story in a short way by telling the main ideas, not details.

Glossary

supporting details: Statements that often follow the main idea. Supporting details give you more information about the main idea.

symbolism: Something that represents something else. For example, a dove is a symbol for peace.

synonyms: Words with the same, or almost the same, meaning (e.g., *sketch* is a synonym of *draw*).

theme: The major idea or topic that the author reveals in a literary work. A theme is usually not stated directly in the work. Instead, the reader has to think about all the details of the work and then make an inference (an educated guess) about what they all mean.

title: A name of a book, film, play, piece of music, or other work of art.

tone: A way of writing that shows a feeling.

topic sentence: A sentence that states the main idea of the paragraph.

valid: Correct, acceptable.

verb: A word that shows action or being.

voice: To express a choice or opinion.

Reading
Assessment One

Directions for Taking the Reading Assessment

The Reading Assessment contains nine reading selections and 40 questions. Some of the selections are fiction, while others are nonfiction. Read each selection and the questions that follow carefully. You may look back at any selection as many times as you would like. If you are unsure of a question, you can move to the next question and go back to the question you skipped later.

Multiple-choice questions require you to pick the best answer out of four possible choices. Only one answer is correct. The short-answer questions will ask you to write your answer and explain your thinking using words. Remember to read the questions and the answer choices carefully. You will mark your answers on the answer document.

When you finish, check your answers.

Read this selection. Then answer the questions that follow.

Alice in Wonderland

By Lewis Carroll

1   The rabbit-hole went straight on like a tunnel for some way, and then dipped suddenly down, so suddenly that Alice had not a moment to think about stopping herself before she found herself falling down a very deep well.

2   Either the well was very deep, or she fell very slowly, for she had plenty of time as she went down to look about her and to wonder what was going to happen next. First, she tried to look down and make out what she was coming to, but it was too dark to see anything; then she looked at the sides of the well, and noticed that they were filled with cupboards and book-shelves; here and there she saw maps and pictures hung upon pegs. She took down a jar from one of the shelves as she passed; it was labeled 'ORANGE MARMALADE', but to her great disappointment it was empty: she did not like to drop the jar for fear of killing somebody, so managed to put it into one of the cupboards as she fell past it.

3   'Well!' thought Alice to herself, 'after such a fall as this, I shall think nothing of tumbling down stairs! How brave they'll all think me at home! Why, I wouldn't say anything about it, even if I fell off the top of the house!' (Which was very likely true.)

4   Down, down, down. Would the fall NEVER come to an end! 'I wonder how many miles I've fallen by this time?' she said aloud. 'I must be getting somewhere near the centre of the earth. Let me see: that would be four thousand miles down, I think—' (for, you see, Alice had learnt several things of this sort in her lessons in the schoolroom, and though this was not a VERY good opportunity for showing off her knowledge, as there was no one to listen to her, still it was good practice to say it over) '—yes, that's about the right distance—but then I wonder what Latitude or Longitude I've got to?' (Alice had no idea what Latitude was, or Longitude either, but thought they were nice grand words to say.)

5   Presently she began again. 'I wonder if I shall fall right THROUGH the earth! How funny it'll seem to come out among the people that walk with their heads downward! The Antipathies, I think—' (she was rather glad there WAS no one listening, this time, as it didn't sound at all the right word) '—but I shall have to ask them what the name of the country is, you know. Please, Ma'am, is this New Zealand or Australia?' (and she tried to curtsey as she spoke—fancy CURTSEYING as you're falling through the air! Do you think you could manage it?) 'And what an ignorant little girl she'll think me for asking! No, it'll never do to ask: perhaps I shall see it written up somewhere.'

Go On ▶

---

6   Down, down, down. There was nothing else to do, so Alice soon began talking again. 'Dinah'll miss me very much to-night, I should think!' (Dinah was the cat.) 'I hope they'll remember her saucer of milk at tea-time. Dinah my dear! I wish you were down here with me! There are no mice in the air, I'm afraid, but you might catch a bat, and that's very like a mouse, you know. But do cats eat bats, I wonder?' And here Alice began to get rather sleepy, and went on saying to herself, in a dreamy sort of way, 'Do cats eat bats? Do cats eat bats?' and sometimes, 'Do bats eat cats?' for, you see, as she couldn't answer either question, it didn't much matter which way she put it. She felt that she was dozing off, and had just begun to dream that she was walking hand in hand with Dinah, and saying to her very earnestly, 'Now, Dinah, tell me the truth: did you ever eat a bat?' when suddenly, thump! thump! down she came upon a heap of sticks and dry leaves, and the fall was over.

Go On ▶

1. What features of the setting help to create a mood of mystery?

    A. the cat that appears while Alice falls down the rabbit-hole

    B. the cupboards, bookshelves, and pictures that hang inside the rabbit-hole

    C. the orange book that she finds while falling down the rabbit-hole

    D. Alice practicing her lessons while falling down the rabbit-hole

2. Read this sentence from the sixth paragraph of the passage.

    "She felt that she was dozing off, and had just begun to dream that she was walking hand in hand with Dinah, and saying to her very earnestly, 'Now, Dinah, tell me the truth: did you ever eat a bat?' when suddenly, thump! thump! down she came upon a heap of sticks and dry leaves, and the fall was over."

    What literary technique is used in this sentence?

    A. onomatopoeia

    B. metaphor

    C. simile

    D. flashback

Go On▶

3. What is the author's purpose for writing the story?

   Provide **one** detail from the story to support your answer.

4. What word BEST describes the setting of this story?

   A. frightening

   B. odd

   C. exciting

   D. sad

5. Which sentence from the passage illustrates that the narrator's point of view is subjective?

   A. "Either the well was very deep, or she fell very slowly, for she had plenty of time as she went down to look about her and wonder what was going to happen next."

   B. "...and she tried to curtsey as she spoke— fancy CURTSEYING as you're falling through the air!"

   C. "...she was rather glad there WAS no one listening, this time, as it didn't sound at all the right word..."

   D. "Alice had no idea what Latitude was, or Longitude either, but thought they were nice grand words to say."

Go On

> **Read this selection. Then answer the questions that follow.**

Of the Origin and Design of Government in General
From "Common Sense," 1776

by Thomas Paine

1   Some writers have so confounded[1] society with government, as to leave little or no distinction between them; whereas they are not only different, but have different origins. Society is produced by our wants, and government by wickedness; the former promotes our happiness positively by uniting our affections, the latter[2] negatively by restraining our vices. The one encourages intercourse[3], the other creates distinctions. The first is a patron[4], the last a punisher.

2   Society in every state is a blessing, but government even in its best state is but a necessary evil; in its worst state an intolerable one; for when we suffer, or are exposed to the same miseries by a government, which we might expect in a country without government, our calamity is heightened by reflecting that we furnish the means by which we suffer. Government, like dress, is the badge of lost innocence; the palaces of kings are built on the ruins of the bowers of paradise. For were the impulses of conscience clear, uniform, and irresistibly obeyed, man would need no other lawgiver; but that not being the case, he finds it necessary to surrender up a part of his property to furnish means for the protection of the rest; and this he is induced[5] to do by the same prudence[6] which in every other case advises him out of two evils to choose the least. Wherefore, security being the true design and end of government, it unanswerably follows that whatever form thereof appears most likely to ensure it to us, with the least expence and greatest benefit, is preferable to all others.

Go On

3   In order to gain a clear and just idea of the design and end of government, let us suppose a small number of persons settled in some sequestered[7] part of the earth, unconnected with the rest, they will then represent the first peopling of any country, or of the world. In this state of natural liberty, society will be their first thought. A thousand motives will excite them thereto, the strength of one man is so unequal to his wants, and his mind so unfitted for perpetual[8] solitude[9], that he is soon obliged to seek assistance and relief of another, who in his turn requires the same. Four or five united would be able to raise a tolerable[10] dwelling in the midst of a wilderness, but one man might labour out the common period of life without accomplishing any thing; when he had felled his timber he could not remove it, nor erect it after it was removed; hunger in the mean time would urge him from his work, and every different want call him a different way. Disease, nay even misfortune would be death, for though neither might be mortal, yet either would disable him from living, and reduce him to a state in which he might rather be said to perish[11] than to die.

Glossary

1.	**confounded:**	confused
2.	**latter:**	the second of two things listed
3.	**intercourse:**	communication or exchanges between people or groups
4.	**patron:**	someone who gives money or support to somebody or something
5.	**induced:**	persuaded or influenced
6.	**prudence:**	using good sense in managing matters
7.	**sequestered:**	an isolated or lonely place away from other people
8.	**perpetual:**	lasting for an indefinitely long time
9.	**solitude:**	the state of being alone
10.	**tolerable:**	moderately good, but not outstanding
11.	**perish:**	to come to an end; to cease to exist

Go On

6. In paragraph 3 of the selection, why does the author include the example of a small group of people unconnected with the rest of the earth?

    Include **two** details from the selection in your answer.

7. Who would find the information in the selection most useful?

    A. someone writing a report on historical views of government

    B. someone writing a report on early colonies in the United States

    C. someone writing a letter to the editor about the current government

    D. someone writing a report about the life of Thomas Paine

8. Read this sentence from the third paragraph of the selection.

    "In order to gain a clear and just idea of the design and end of government, let us suppose a small number of persons settled in some sequestered part of the earth, unconnected with the rest, they will then represent the first peopling of any country, or of the world."

    What does the word *sequestered* mean?

    A. a forest with many wild animals

    B. an isolated place away from other people

    C. a city located in the desert

    D. a populated area with many industries

Go On ▶

9. Based on the selection, what inference can the reader make about the author?

    A. He would support the idea of the government having a larger role in people's lives.

    B. He has no interest in what the government does.

    C. He believes there is no reason that governments should exist.

    D. He would not support the idea of the government having a larger role in people's lives.

10. Why did Thomas Paine write this passage?

    A. to argue the difference between society and government

    B. to persuade the reader to support government

    C. to tell a story about the beginning of a society

    D. to explain the process of creating a new government

Go On

> **Read this selection. Then answer the questions that follow.**

Give Me the Splendid Silent Sun

by Walt Whitman

Part 1

1   GIVE me the splendid silent sun with all his beams full-dazzling,

2   Give me juicy autumnal fruit ripe and red from the orchard,

3   Give me a field where the unmow'd grass grows,

4   Give me an arbor, give me the trellis'd[1] grape,

5   Give me fresh corn and wheat, give me serene-moving animals teaching content,

6   Give me nights perfectly quiet as on high plateaus west of the Mississippi, and I looking up at the stars,

7   Give me odorous[2] at sunrise a garden of beautiful flowers where I can walk undisturb'd,

8   Give me for marriage a sweet-breath'd woman of whom I should never tire,

9   Give me a perfect child, give me away aside from the noise of the world a rural domestic life,

10   Give me to warble spontaneous songs recluse[3] by myself, for my own ears only,

11   Give me solitude, give me Nature, give me again O Nature your primal sanities!

12   These demanding to have them (tired with ceaseless excitement, and rack'd by the war-strife[4]),

13   These to procure[5] incessantly[6] asking, rising in cries from my heart,

14   While yet incessantly asking still I adhere to my city,

15   Day upon day and year upon year O city, walking your streets,

16   Where you hold me enchain'd a certain time refusing to give me up,

17   Yet giving to make me glutted[7], enrich'd of soul, you give me forever faces;

18   (Oh I see what I sought to escape, confronting, reversing my cries,

19   I see my own soul trampling down what it ask'd for).

[1] trellis: an arch used as a support for vines and other creeping plants

[2] odorous: having a distinct odor

[3] recluse: withdrawn from the world

[4] strife: a conflict; a violent struggle

[5] procure: to obtain or acquire

[6] incessantly: continuing without interruption

[7] glutted: filled beyond capacity

Go On

Part 2

20   Keep your splendid silent sun,

21   Keep your woods O Nature, and the quiet places by the woods,

22   Keep your fields of clover and timothy[8], and your corn-fields and orchards,

23   Keep the blossoming buckwheat fields where the Ninth-month bees hum;

24   Give me faces and streets—give me these phantoms incessant and endless along the trottoirs[9]!

25   Give me interminable[10] eyes—give me women—give me comrades and lovers by the thousand!

26   Let me see new ones every day—let me hold new ones by the hand every day!

27   Give me such shows—give me the streets of Manhattan!

28   Give me Broadway, with the soldiers marching—give me the sound of the trumpets and drums!

29   (The soldiers in companies or regiments—some starting away, flush'd and reckless,

30   Some, their time up, returning with thinn'd ranks, young, yet very old, worn, marching, noticing nothing;)

31   Give me the shores and wharves[11] heavy-fringed with black ships!

32   O such for me! O an intense life, full to repletion[12] and varied!

33   The life of the theatre, bar-room, huge hotel, for me!

34   The saloon of the steamer! the crowded excursion for me! the torchlight procession!

35   The dense brigade bound for the war, with high piled military wagons following;

36   People, endless, streaming, with strong voices, passions, pageants,

37   Manhattan streets with their powerful throbs, with beating drums as now,

38   The endless and noisy chorus, the rustle and clank of muskets (even the sight of the wounded),

39   Manhattan crowds, with their turbulent musical chorus!

40   Manhattan faces and eyes forever for me.

[8] timothy: a North American grass

[9] trottoir: footpath; sidewalk

[10] interminable: seeming to be without an end

[11] wharves: landing places for ships

[12] repletion: being fully satisfied or completely filled

Go On ▶

11. How are the narrators from the two sections of the poem alike?

   A. Both enjoy the sounds of trumpets and drums.

   B. Both enjoy looking up at the stars at night.

   C. Both are looking for a setting in which to live a happy life.

   D. Both are looking to spend the rest of their lives in the places they are now.

12. Read this sentence from lines 10 and 11 of the poem.

   "Give me to warble spontaneous songs *recluse* by myself, for my own ears only,

   Give me solitude, give me Nature, give me again O Nature your primal sanities!"

   What does the word *recluse* mean?

   A. happily

   B. withdrawn from the world

   C. without instruments

   D. with friends

Go On

13. Based on the information in the poem, what generalization can the reader make about the narrator from part 2?

   A. The narrator in part 2 enjoys being around large groups of people.

   B. The narrator in part 2 enjoys working on a farm.

   C. The narrator in part 2 feels imprisoned by the city.

   D. The narrator in part 2 enjoys walking in the quiet woods.

14. Read line 23 from the poem.

   "Keep the blossoming buckwheat fields where the Ninth-month bees hum;"

   What literary techniques are used in this line?

   A. personification and metaphor

   B. simile and flashback

   C. alliteration and onomatopoeia

   D. foreshadowing and alliteration

Go On ▶

Read this selection. Then answer the questions that follow.

AURORA BOREALIS:
NATURE'S LIGHT SHOW

1   Did you know that one of the best shows in the Northern Hemisphere isn't on TV or at the movies—it's in the sky? This phenomenon, called aurora borealis, is more commonly known as the northern lights. These lights occur in a ring around the North Pole, which stretches over parts of Alaska and Canada. In the Southern Hemisphere, the lights produced are called aurora australis. Aurora polaris, which means polar lights, is a term that can be used for both the northern and southern lights.

2   The aurora borealis is caused by particles blown toward Earth by solar winds. The Sun gives off high-energy charged particles. These particles, also known as ions, travel into space at speeds of 200 to 440 miles per second. The particles carry an electrical charge, which interacts with the magnetic field surrounding Earth. When these particles hit the magnetic rings around the North and South Poles, they fall into Earth's upper atmosphere. On the way down, they run into oxygen and nitrogen to produce brilliant waves of color. The colors of the lights, which can be blues, violets, greens, and reds, depend on what the particles run into and at what height.

3   The solar winds blow particles from the Sun at nearly one million miles per hour, so when the particles reach Earth they are in constant motion. This is part of the reason why the lights appear in curtain-like waves. Another reason is that the charged particles can make Earth's magnetic field bend and change shape. These changes can cause the spirals and other round shapes that are often seen as part of the auroras.

4   Although people have reported seeing the aurora borealis reach down into clouds and mountains, the lowest edge is usually between 40 and 60 miles above Earth—much higher than any mountains, clouds, or even airplanes. The only people to fly through the aurora are astronauts, whose space shuttles fly 190 miles above Earth. Auroras can be more than 1,000 miles in length, but they are only about a mile wide.

Go On▶

5 Scientists have learned more about the auroras in the past half century than they have at any other time, but they still do not know what causes some of the shapes people see in the lights. People have reported seeing shapes that resemble animals, in addition to the normal thin waves. Sounds accompanying the lights have also been reported, even though the air in the atmosphere where the lights are seen is too thin to carry any sound.

6 Before scientists discovered the cause of the lights, the various colors and shapes in the aurora borealis led to a number of myths. Some Canadian Eskimos believed the lights were torches lighting a path to heaven. Other cultures, especially some in Europe who only saw the lights occasionally, thought they were omens of disaster.

7 Usually, the aurora borealis can only be seen by those close to the North Pole. Many people believe that Fairbanks, Alaska, is one of the prime locations for viewing. There are also a few locations in eastern Canada that are known for their views of the aurora borealis. Sometimes the ring can stretch to cover parts of Europe and the continental United States. This happens in years when the Sun is very active. When the Sun is active, it can send huge gusts of solar wind toward Earth, causing spectacular displays of the northern lights that can be seen much farther south than usual.

8 Unfortunately, for the majority of people living in the United States, the possibility of seeing the northern lights occurs between 3 and 18 times a year. But the possibility alone does not mean someone will see the lights. Things, like an overcast sky, artificial light in the night sky, and pollution further reduce your chances of witnessing this awesome occurrence, as does living south of the North Pole. The further one gets from the North Pole, the more one's chances of seeing the aurora borealis is reduced.

9 Auroras are most common during the spring and fall, although they can happen at any time of year. Auroras can only be seen on clear nights, and the best time to see them is between midnight and two in the morning. Scientists can now predict when they think auroras will be visible, so in the future, many more people may have the opportunity to see these brilliant displays of light.

Go On

15. How does the aurora borealis compare to the aurora australis?

   A. They both describe the light show in the Northern Hemisphere.

   B. They both describe the light show in the Southern Hemisphere.

   C. They both describe the light show in neither hemisphere.

   D. One describes the light show in the Northern Hemisphere, while the other describes the light show in the Southern Hemisphere.

16. Why did Canadian Eskimos and early European cultures develop myths about the aurora borealis?

   A. The myths were a way for them to explain the brilliant waves of color in the sky.

   B. The myths explained why bad things happened after seeing the lights.

   C. The myths were a scientific explanation for the aurora borealis.

   D. They were used to seeing the aurora borealis, and they liked to tell stories about the colors in the sky.

17. Why did the author write the passage?

   A. to inform readers about the aurora borealis

   B. to explain where readers can view the aurora borealis

   C. to persuade readers to visit Fairbanks, Alaska

   D. to deter readers from learning about scientific phenomena

18. Read the sentence from the selection.

"On the way down, they *run into* oxygen and nitrogen to produce brilliant waves of color."

What does the phrase *run into* mean in the sentence above?

   A. separate pieces

   B. repel quickly

   C. unexpectedly find

   D. collide with

Go On ▶

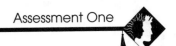

19. What is the main idea of the seventh paragraph?

    A. The aurora borealis is most often seen near the North Pole, but this isn't the only place it is visible.

    B. The aurora borealis stretches south when the solar winds are active.

    C. Only those close to the North Pole can see the aurora borealis.

    D. The spectacular displays of the northern lights can be seen very far south of the North Pole.

20. Why will most people never fly through an aurora borealis?

    A. The aurora borealis moves too fast; an airplane would never be able to catch it.

    B. The aurora borealis is only an optical illusion; there is nothing for an airplane to fly through.

    C. The lowest edge of the aurora borealis is too far above Earth to be reached in an airplane.

    D. The aurora borealis is too small for an airplane to pass through it.

Go On

Read this selection. Then answer the questions that follow.

Der Blitz Bugs

1   It was a cool summer evening at the family lake house in northern New York. We were all exhausted from the day-long boat trip and sat immobile on the front porch chairs. My body felt like the tiredness went deep down inside—into every muscle, into every joint, into every bone. I was a stone statue on a wooden rocking chair.

2   I watched the moonbeams dance on the ripples of the calm lake in front of the porch. Everything else was black, except for the candles that lit up the porch and my family's happy tired faces.

3   I looked out to the lake again and noticed a small blink of light by the tree. I continued to watch because I wasn't sure if I really saw it or not. Then, sure enough, the small light blinked again. Then two more blinked in unison after that.

4   "Schau," my grandmother said. "Der blitz bugs."

5   My grandparents moved to America from Germany when my mother was two years old. They know how to speak enough English to get around town, but they always speak in a German-English mixture among family members. We understand what they're saying…most of the time.

6   "Yeah, I see them Oma. They're lightning bugs."

7   "Ja," she answered. "Would you like to der blitz bugs catch? It ist very fun."

8   She looked very excited, like the little blinks of light brought back a distant happy memory from the past.

Go On ▶

       © Englefield & Associates, Inc.

9   "Sure Oma, let's bring Sam and John too."

10   Sam and John were my younger twin brothers. They were always finding new ways to get into trouble. At that moment, they were playing with marbles on the floor.

11   It was hard to get out of my chair, but the tiredness went away when I finally pushed myself out and walked over to get my brothers.

***

12   Sam and John bolted into the yard and headed for the tree where all the twinkling lights seemed to stay. My Oma and I followed.

13   Sam and John ran around the tree as if they were Native Americans dancing around a wild campfire. They would catch one bug, then another bug would light up nearby, so they would let the first bug go and stalk their new target.

14   I looked around when Oma and I got within a few feet of the tree. The lightning bugs surrounded us on every side. Between the darkness of the night and the tiny flickers of lights, I felt like I had slipped into the star-covered night sky.

15   My grandma smiled.

16   "Der wonderful blitz bugs," she simply said.

Go On ▶

21. How are the candles and the lightning bugs similar in the story?

   A. Their lights are both described as "flickering."

   B. Both of their lights shine on family members' faces.

   C. The lights are as bright as the moonbeams on the water.

   D. They both are the only forms of light surrounded by darkness.

22. Which sentence from the story is an example of a metaphor?

   A. "Sam and John ran around the tree as if they were Native Americans dancing around a wild campfire."

   B. "I was a stone statue on a wooden rocking chair."

   C. "It was a cool summer evening at the family lake house in northern New York."

   D. "I watched the moonbeams dance on the ripples of the calm lake in front of the porch."

Go On▶

23. Why is the narrator so exhausted?

   A. because he has been running around trying to catch lightning bugs

   B. because he didn't sleep well the night before

   C. because he spent the day outside on a boat trip

   D. because he had played outside with his twin brothers

24. Why does grandma call the lightning bugs "der blitz bugs"?

   A. She has memory loss and cannot remember the correct name of the bug.

   B. She is originally from Germany and speaks in a German-English mixture among family members.

   C. She creates her own language and makes up a new name for lightning bugs.

   D. She is originally from Switzerland and speaks in a German-English mixture among family members.

Go On

Read this selection. Then answer the questions that follow.

"Worry Dolls"

1   *Worry dolls, or trouble dolls, are small dolls made of wood or wire with thread or fabric clothing. They were originally made in Guatemala. According to folklore, if a person cannot sleep because they are worrying about something, they can tell their worries to a worry doll and place it under their pillow before going to sleep. The person will wake up with no more worries, since the dolls have taken them away during the night.*

2   There was a young girl named Ana, who lived just outside a small village in the hills of Guatemala. She lived with her mother, grandfather, and younger brother, Felipe. Ana's family was not wealthy; they had to work very hard to make ends meet. They all worked together, though.

3   The family's only income came from the cloth that Ana's mother wove so beautifully. They had a few crops, but were barely able to grow enough to eat, let alone sell for a profit. Every day the children and their grandfather would tend to the crops while Ana's mother would weave her beautiful cloth.

4   At the end of the day, when the chores were done and Ana and Felipe were on the verge of sleep, Ana's mother would place all of her cloth in a basket under Felipe's bed and go to bed.

5   One night, Felipe woke with a start when he heard a noise. There was a dark shadow moving across the room. Felipe screamed, "It's a robber!" But it was too late. The robber slipped out of the house, taking with him the cloth that Ana's and Felipe's mother had carefully woven.

6   When the sun came up the next day, Ana's mother was very ill. Her two seasons of work were gone, and the family had no source of income for the rest of the year. Ana pulled Felipe aside. "I have an idea for how we can help," she said. She had brought with her what remained from the basket: a few small scraps of brightly colored cloth.

Go On ▶

---

7   "Go collect some small twigs and bring them back to me," Ana said. Felipe did as he was told and brought back some twigs, and the children got to work making dozens of tiny dolls and little pouches for them to sleep in. She remembered a story her grandfather had told her about magic dolls and she hoped that, for the sake of her family, these dolls would be magical.

8   When it was time for bed, Ana pulled all of the dolls out of one of the pouches. She lined them up in her hand and spoke. "My family is in trouble and we need your help. My mother is sick, we don't have enough to eat, and my mother's cloth was stolen so we have no money. Please help us." She placed the dolls back in their pouch, placed them under her pillow, and went to sleep.

9   Ana slept very soundly that night, and when she awoke, the dolls were out of their pouch and lined up on the table. Ana was certain she had placed them under her pillow, so she was quite perplexed. But, she didn't have time to think about it, so she gathered all the dolls and she and Felipe headed to the market to try to sell the "magic" dolls and help their family.

10   At the end of the day, the dolls still had not sold, so with a feeling of defeat, Ana and Felipe began to put away the dolls to head home. She knew her hopes of selling all the dolls had been unrealistic, but she had expected to sell at least one pouch. Just then a man wearing a large hat approached.

11   "What are you selling?" he asked.

12   "Magic dolls!" Ana said.

13   "Well I could surely use some magic," the man replied. "I'll take all of them."

14   Ana and Felipe wrapped the dolls and the man handed them some money. Before Ana could count out some change, the man was gone. She counted the money. Almost $1,000! In Guatemala, that was enough for the family to live off of for a year! Ana and Felipe bought some food to take home to their mother and grandfather and share the good news. When they arrived home, there was more good news: their mother was feeling better.

15   As Ana got ready for bed that night, she found something in her pocket. It was the same pouch of dolls she had spoken to the night before! She was certain she had sold them to the man at the market. In the pouch was a note.

16   *Tell these dolls your secret wishes, dreams, and problems. When you wake up, you may find the magic within you to make your dreams come true and your problems disappear.*

17   There was no name, just a drawing of a man in a big hat.

Go On ▶

25. To Ana, the dolls are a symbol of —

    A. health.

    B. food.

    C. hope.

    D. wealth.

26. In paragraph 4, the author uses the words *woke with a start* to show that Felipe is —

    A. excited.

    B. startled.

    C. hungry.

    D. tired.

Go On

    Copying is Prohibited   © Englefield & Associates, Inc.

27. How is the main problem in this story solved?

   A. Ana asks a mysterious man at the market if he will help her family buy some food and help make her mother well.

   B. Ana makes magic dolls to sell at the market and a mysterious man pays enough money for the dolls that the family can live on it for a year.

   C. Ana persuades Felipe to make dolls that magically take away all of the family's problems by asking others for money.

   D. Ana and Felipe promise their mother they will help her weave new cloth to replace all that was stolen by the robber.

28. What is the theme that is used throughout the story?

   A. Worrying won't help you solve your problems.

   B. Prepare for the worst that could happen.

   C. Always try to solve your family's problems.

   D. Never give up hope when things are bad.

Go On

Read this selection. Then answer the questions that follow.

"Dreamcatcher"

1   *Dreamcatchers are an American-Indian tradition, from the Ojibway (Chippewa) tribe. Ojibway created dreamcatchers from sinew strands tied in a web around a small round frame. They would hang the dreamcatchers above children's beds to protect them from nightmares. The legend is that the bad dreams will get caught in the web, and the good dreams will pass through the hole in the center of the dreamcatcher to the sleeping children.*

2   Ahmik's eyes flew open. What a terrible dream he had been having! It seemed so real! Ahmik could vividly recall the details of the large black bear barreling after him as he ran screaming to warn his chief of the danger. He sat upright, slipped on his moccasins, and peered out the front door of his wigwam. There was no black bear in sight, and Ahmik breathed a sigh of relief.

3   He had been having these nightmares quite often. It wasn't always the same dream, but he always woke frightened and drenched in sweat. He hadn't told anyone about them, for fear they would tease him. His grandmother, who he was very close to, didn't even know. But the dreams were getting worse, and Ahmik knew he had to do something about them.

4   The next morning, after getting barely a wink of sleep since the nightmare, Ahmik went to his grandmother. "Grandmother, I have been having awful dreams and I don't know how to make them stop," he said. "I used to have such lovely dreams, but lately, all of my dreams are terrible nightmares."

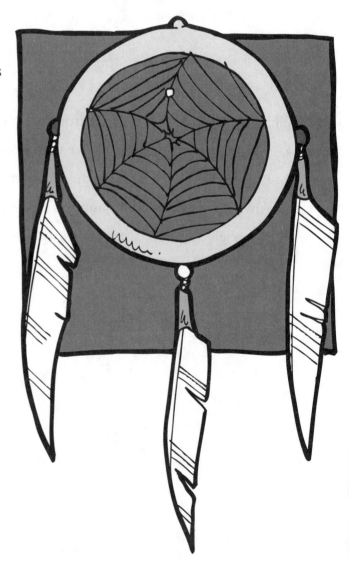

Go On ▶

---

5   Ahmik's grandmother looked at him with concern. She promised him she would try to help rid him of the nightmares so he could sleep soundly again. She sent Ahmik off with his father to hunt for game, and she went to work farming in the fields.

6   As she was tending to the crops, she came across a spider that was spinning a web on one of the plants. As another woman in the tribe went to destroy the web, the grandmother spoke.

7   "Stop! Don't hurt it!" The grandmother wanted to help the spider, so she moved the web to a nearby tree where it would be safe.

8   The spider was very grateful for the grandmother's kindness so he told her that he would give her a present. "I will spin a web for you, with an intricate design that will snare bad dreams and let good ones through a small hole in the middle."

9   The grandmother was overjoyed. When the day's work was over, she quickly returned to the village where she met Ahmik. She excitedly showed him the gift the spider had given her. Ahmik's' grandmother placed the web on a sinew hoop and hung it over Ahmik's bed.

10   "With this dreamcatcher, you will not have bad dreams," she said.

11   Ahmik was uncertain if the web would work but was willing to give it a try. After all, his grandmother was the wisest person he knew, besides the chief.

12   That night, Ahmik slept more soundly than he had ever slept before. He had wonderful dreams all night. In one, he met the same spider that had spun the web for his grandmother and was able to thank him for the priceless gift.

Go On ▶

29. Use of the third-person omniscient point of view allows the author to —

   A. concentrate on the facts of the story.

   B. show how the chief of the village was very wise.

   C. describe the setting accurately and in great detail.

   D. include both Ahmik's and his grandmother's thoughts and feelings.

30. This story is organized by —

   A. comparing Ahmik's dreams before he had the dreamcatcher to his dreams after.

   B. providing examples of the types of dreams Ahmik had been having.

   C. describing how Ahmik's grandmother was able to help stop his nightmares.

   D. discussing what Ahmik thinks about his new dreamcatcher his grandmother gave him.

Go On

31. The main problem in the stories "Worry Dolls" and "Dreamcatcher" is solved by —

  A. hard work.

  B. kindness to others.

  C. something magical.

  D. the main character.

32. How does Ana in the story "Worry Dolls" and Ahmik in the story "Dreamcatchers" approach solving their problems differently?

  A. Ana is trying to make money, while Ahmik is trying to get a good night's sleep.

  B. Ana tries to solve the problem herself, while Ahmik asks for the help of his grandmother.

  C. Ana focuses on using what is available to her, while Ahmik seeks the help of a spider.

  D. Ana wanted to help her mother, while Ahmik wanted to help himself.

Go On

> **Read this selection. Then answer the questions that follow.**

Zora Neale Hurston

1   Zora Neale Hurston was born on January 7, 1891. Zora was raised in Eatonville, Florida, a town with historical significance. It was the first all-black incorporated city in the United States. Zora, a future writer and folklorist, was the daughter of a Baptist preacher and a schoolteacher. Unfortunately, Zora's mother died when Zora was in her early teens. The fifth child of eight, Zora moved in with one of her brothers upon her mother's death. She helped raise her nieces and nephews, a task which left her eager to remove herself from the responsibilities of caring for a household. At age 16, Zora joined a traveling theater company. In addition to her work as a performer, Zora worked as a maid for well-to-do households, as a manicurist, and pursued an education.

2   In 1925, Zora headed to New York City. She attended Barnard College, where she studied anthropology. After college, Zora began working as an ethnologist, combining her knowledge of culture with her passion of fiction writing. She quickly became an important part of the Harlem Renaissance, which was an African-American cultural movement of the 1920s and 1930s that brought African-American literature, music, art, and politics to the attention of the American public. Zora was a skilled storyteller. She traveled throughout New York, Florida, and the Caribbean collecting oral histories. She collaborated with Langston Hughes to write a play in 1931, and her first novel, Jonah's Gourd Vine, was published in 1934.

Go On ▶

3   Zora's best-known work, *Their Eyes Were Watching God*, was published in 1937. At that time, the novel was criticized for not taking a political stand against racism and poverty. Instead, Zora chose to focus on her main character's search for love and happiness as a black woman of the South. Today, most people choose to celebrate the novel's rich tradition of the rural black South as presented in Zora's words.

4   Zora went on to publish several other novels in the 1940s. These books enjoyed modest success, but her writing career eventually declined. She was a member of the faculty of North Carolina College for Negroes in Durham, she wrote for Warner Brothers Motion Pictures, and she was also a staff member at the Library of Congress. She eventually moved back to Florida. She worked as a maid until her health made such chores impossible. She lived out her remaining days penniless and alone. She suffered from a stroke and died in 1959. She was buried in an unmarked grave in Fort Pierce, Florida.

Go On

33. Explain how Zora Neale Hurston's home life and studies in college influenced her writings.

34. Which of these sentences expresses an opinion?

A. "Zora went on to publish several other novels in the 1940s."

B. "At that time, the novel was criticized for not taking a political stand against racism and poverty."

C. "She traveled to New York, Florida, and the Caribbean collecting oral histories."

D. "Unfortunately, Zora's mother died when she was in her early teens."

Go On

> **Read this selection. Then answer the questions that follow.**

The Old House

Part I: Leaving the Woods

1   I emerged at the far end of the dirt path, just past the line of trees. The old house loomed not more than a hundred yards beyond. I expected that it might look smaller, or at least less ominous, now that I was a few years older and wasn't so caught up in silly, youthful superstition. But this was not the case; it had only acquired more cracks and gaps and broken boards to add to its enormous, rundown appearance.

2   Back in elementary school, my friend Jack and I had passed this house almost every day on our way home from school. Some days, we ran past as quickly as we could, convinced that something inside was going to get us. Other days, we explored, daring each other to peek through broken windows and holes in the siding. The middle school we attend now is farther away, so we carpool. Today, though, Jack was sick, and my mom had to pick up her friend from the airport. It was a cold and snowy day, but with the only alternative being a two-hour wait for my mom to pick me up, I chose the walk.

3   As I approached the house, I drifted in my course so that I was walking in the large vacant yard that separated the house from the sidewalk. Feeling almost as if some external force was compelling me to do so, I angled my path closer and closer to the abandoned structure. The contrast between the dinginess of the house and the bright white snow gave it a surreal quality.

Part II: An Unfamiliar Noise

4   A minute or two later, I found myself only a few feet away from the house. I tiptoed around the perimeter, peering in windows. The inside was exactly as I remembered it—broken and rotting wood furniture, everything covered in a thick coat of dust. I was staring so intently that I didn't see the gigantic icicle beginning to break free from the overhang just to my right.

Go On ▶

5   SNAP! WHOOSH! THUD! A noise unlike any I had ever heard sounded above my head, only a few feet away. My heart jumped into my throat, and I instinctively began running as fast as I could. After a few seconds, I glanced back over my shoulder and saw the huge chunk of ice still trembling where it had landed in the snow. Knowing the cause of the noise, I slowed my pace slightly, but the event had jarred my thoughts; I wanted to get off that particular street as quickly as I could.

6   Still running, I reached the end of the block and burst out onto the main street through town. I stopped and looked around—everyone was going about their tasks, paying no attention to me standing on the corner, trying to catch my breath. I stood up straight and began to walk again. By the time I reached my street, I was laughing out loud at my childish fright. I decided to call Jack when I got home; I knew he would get a laugh out of the situation, too.

Go On ▶

35. The narrator says the main idea of "Part II: An Unfamiliar Noise" is that he becomes frightened of the old house again, even though he is older. Which of the following sentences from the passage supports this idea?

   A. "The inside was exactly as I remembered it—broken and rotting wood furniture, everything covered in a thick coat of dust."

   B. "A minute or two later, I found myself only a few feet away from the house."

   C. "After a few seconds, I glanced back over my shoulder and saw the huge chunk of ice still trembling where it had landed in the snow."

   D. "My heart jumped into my throat, and I instinctively began running as fast as I could."

36. Why must the narrator walk by the old house again?

   A. His mother's car broke down and he would have to wait two hours in the cold weather for her.

   B. Jack is sick and the narrator's mother has to pick a friend up at the airport.

   C. Jack is sick and the narrator's mother is arriving at the airport.

   D. He wants to see how the old house has changed since he last saw it.

Go On ▶

37. Which sentence from the story is an example of imagery?

   A. "A minute or two later, I found myself only a few feet away from the house."

   B. "It had only acquired more cracks and gaps and broken boards to add to its enormous, rundown appearance."

   C. "I stopped and looked around—everyone was going about their tasks, paying no attention to me standing on the corner, trying to catch my breath."

   D. "Today, though, Jack was sick, and my mom had to pick up her friend from the airport."

38. Why does the author use the first person point of view?

   A. because Jack is telling the story to the reader

   B. so the reader can know the narrator's thoughts and feelings

   C. because that is the only way the story could be told

   D. so the reader can hear the noise the icicle makes when it falls

39. What literary technique is used in the second paragraph of "Part I: Leaving the Woods?"

   A. foreshadowing

   B. metaphor

   C. flashback

   D. onomatopoeia

40. Which idea is included in the section titled "An Unfamiliar Noise"?

   A. The narrator finds that the inside of the house is the same as he remembers it.

   B. The narrator believes the house might seem smaller now that he is older.

   C. The narrator thinks that the contrast of the house with the snow gives the house a surreal quality.

   D. The narrator feels as if some type of force is pulling him closer to the house.

1 Ⓐ Ⓑ Ⓒ Ⓓ

2 Ⓐ Ⓑ Ⓒ Ⓓ

3

4 Ⓐ Ⓑ Ⓒ Ⓓ

5 Ⓐ Ⓑ Ⓒ Ⓓ

6

7 Ⓐ Ⓑ Ⓒ Ⓓ

8 Ⓐ Ⓑ Ⓒ Ⓓ

9 Ⓐ Ⓑ Ⓒ Ⓓ

10 Ⓐ Ⓑ Ⓒ Ⓓ

11 Ⓐ Ⓑ Ⓒ Ⓓ

12 Ⓐ Ⓑ Ⓒ Ⓓ

13 Ⓐ Ⓑ Ⓒ Ⓓ

14 Ⓐ Ⓑ Ⓒ Ⓓ

15 Ⓐ Ⓑ Ⓒ Ⓓ

16 Ⓐ Ⓑ Ⓒ Ⓓ

17 Ⓐ Ⓑ Ⓒ Ⓓ

18 Ⓐ Ⓑ Ⓒ Ⓓ

19 Ⓐ Ⓑ Ⓒ Ⓓ

20 Ⓐ Ⓑ Ⓒ Ⓓ

21 Ⓐ Ⓑ Ⓒ Ⓓ

22 Ⓐ Ⓑ Ⓒ Ⓓ

23 Ⓐ Ⓑ Ⓒ Ⓓ

24 Ⓐ Ⓑ Ⓒ Ⓓ

25 Ⓐ Ⓑ Ⓒ Ⓓ

26 Ⓐ Ⓑ Ⓒ Ⓓ

27 Ⓐ Ⓑ Ⓒ Ⓓ

28 Ⓐ Ⓑ Ⓒ Ⓓ

29 Ⓐ Ⓑ Ⓒ Ⓓ

30 Ⓐ Ⓑ Ⓒ Ⓓ

31 Ⓐ Ⓑ Ⓒ Ⓓ

32 Ⓐ Ⓑ Ⓒ Ⓓ

33

34 Ⓐ Ⓑ Ⓒ Ⓓ

35 Ⓐ Ⓑ Ⓒ Ⓓ

36 Ⓐ Ⓑ Ⓒ Ⓓ

37 Ⓐ Ⓑ Ⓒ Ⓓ

38 Ⓐ Ⓑ Ⓒ Ⓓ

39 Ⓐ Ⓑ Ⓒ Ⓓ

40 Ⓐ Ⓑ Ⓒ Ⓓ

Reading Assessment Two

Directions for Taking the Reading Assessment

The Reading Assessment contains seven reading selections and 40 questions. Some of the selections are fiction, while others are nonfiction. Read each selection and the questions that follow carefully. You may look back at any selection as many times as you would like. If you are unsure of a question, you can move to the next question, and go back to the question you skipped later.

Multiple-choice questions require you to pick the best answer out of four possible choices. Only one answer is correct. The short-answer questions will ask you to write your answer and explain your thinking using words. Remember to read the questions and the answer choices carefully. You will mark your answers on the answer document.

When you finish, check your answers.

Read this selection. Then answer the questions that follow.

The Secret Share

1   Aishe waited in line to pay for the small paint set, the paintbrush, and the art pad. The thin, delicate hairs of the paintbrush felt like soft feathers in her hand.

2   "Gift wrap?" asked the sales clerk behind the counter.

3   "Yes," Aishe replied, scanning the selection. "Please use that silver paper, and tie it with a blue ribbon."

4   She watched the clerk carefully wrap each item and place it in a white box. The clerk tore a sheet of the glossy, silver paper from a large roll. She lined up the box with the paper's center and efficiently turned the boring white box into a spectacular silver cube. Leaning her arms on the counter, Aishe selected one of the small gift cards that said "Arno's Art Shop." On the inside of the card, she wrote, "See the world through the eyes of an artist. Your friend, Aishe." She tucked the little card under the cube's blue ribbon.

5   The day before summer vacation, Aishe carried the silver package to school. She was proud of her present, and she held it carefully in her hands. She didn't want anything to disturb the perfect mirror created on each side of the cube. Sunlight hit the package and reflections danced about Aishe's face. Aishe admired the gift with such adoration that if people were to look at her, they would hardly have believed she would willingly give it up. But they didn't know she had bought this gift for someone. This gift had a purpose.

6   Mrs. Thurston was hosting a secret-share party for her seventh-grade social studies class. It was tradition; every year, Mrs. Thurston celebrated the close of the school year with this unique festivity. Each student was assigned a partner, but Mrs. Thurston didn't want the seventh graders to reveal their partners, so the list was a secret until the last minute, when it was time for students to exchange gifts at the class party.

7   "Mrs. Thurston is the best," said Aishe's best friend Sunil. "I'm really going to miss her next year." The girls walked together toward the cafeteria. The halls were louder than normal. They buzzed with the sounds of eager students. "She is so interested in history and in people who lived in the past . . ."

Go On ▶

                                       © Englefield & Associates, Inc.

8   ". . . but she also pays attention to people who are alive today, like us," finished Aishe.

9   Aishe felt certain that Mrs. Thurston would pair best friends together. At the secret share party, Aishe would be able to exchange gifts with Sunil. Unwrapping the new supplies, Sunil might begin to enjoy art, instead of always laughing at it. On weekends, Sunil liked to say, "Come on, put away those paints, Aishe. Paint is boring and messy. Wouldn't you rather play softball?"

6   After Wednesday's lunch, the hall once again filled with the noise of clanging lockers. Before the bell rang, students returned to the classroom with packages. Parcels sat on each desk. The size and shape of each was as varied as the presenters. Aishe glanced with annoyance at the girl beside her, the new student named Britte. As usual, the girl sat in silence at her desk. She had wrapped her parcel in brown paper. Aishe could see that Britte had cut a brown grocery bag to fit the size of the gift. Brown tape sealed the edges together.

7   "Boring brown paper to match Britte's boring personality," whispered a voice in the second row. Aishe could hear a ripple of giggling along the row.

8   "It's probably an empty box," whispered another voice behind Aishe. "A gift of nothing from the girl with nothing to say." The giggling was louder now.

Go On

9   Aishe wondered who would get stuck with Britte's brown package. Maybe the teacher would be Britte's secret partner; no one else wanted to be the new girl's friend. Mrs. Thurston handed a piece of paper to a student in the front row.

10   "Class, this is our secret-share list," announced Mrs. Thurston. "Please find your name on the list. Your partner's name is listed beside yours. When the bell rings, pass your gift along to your partner."

11   With excitement, students passed the list from desk to desk. When it reached Britte, the new girl looked over at Aishe. Her eyes were shining. When Aishe saw the list, she knew why: Aishe and Britte were partners. "Oh no," Aishe grumbled inside. Aishe felt her face grow hot. She wanted to shout, "This isn't fair. I bought this for Sunil." She wanted to run out of the room. She wanted to hide her perfect cube. But she didn't do any of those things.

12   The bell rang. Slowly, without raising her eyes from the desk, she handed her beautiful silver package to the new girl. Britte slid the big, ugly brown paper bag across Aishe's desk. She looked at its crude construction. Even the tape was ugly. Resentfully, she opened the boring gift from boring Britte.

13   Inside the brown paper, she found an inner package. It was wrapped in bright pink paper and was tied with a silver ribbon. Carefully, Aishe unwrapped the surprise. Inside, a card lay on top of a small box of . . . art supplies.

14   Cobalt Blue. Carmine Red. Burnt Sienna. The names of the colors seemed to glisten on the labels. Aishe read the card.

15   "Dear Classmate, I have loved painting ever since I was a little girl. I hope you enjoy these supplies as much as I enjoyed carefully selecting them. If you would like, I would be happy to show you how to mix these tubes of color. Painting is a wonderful hobby, and I'm sure you're really going to enjoy it. Sincerely, your new classmate, Britte."

16   Aishe held her breath. Turning toward the new girl, Aishe watched Britte unwrap the silver paper and open her gift.

Go On ▶

Copying is Prohibited   © Englefield & Associates, Inc.

1. What detail does the author include that lets the reader know there may be more to Britte than Aishe realizes?

    A. Britte wraps her package in a brown paper bag.

    B. Britte doesn't talk with other members of the seventh-grade social studies class.

    C. Aishe laughs when the other students make fun of Britte.

    D. Aishe finds a brightly colored package underneath the brown paper wrapping.

2. Read the sentence from the story.

    "Sunlight hit the package and *reflections danced about Aishe's face*."

    What does the phrase *reflections danced about Aishe's face* from the sentence above mean?

    A. Sunlight patterns moved around on Aishe's face.

    B. Sunlight patterns tap-danced on Aishe's face.

    C. Sunlight patterns blinded Aishe and forced her to stop walking to school.

    D. Sunlight patterns tripped Aishe and caused her to fall on her face.

Go On

3. What problem does Aishe face in this story?

    A. She doesn't know what type of gift to buy for the secret share party.

    B. Aishe's friend, Sunil, refuses to paint portraits with Aishe.

    C. Aishe's friend, Sunil, doesn't like the art supplies Aishe bought for her.

    D. Aishe's partner for the gift exchange is Britte, a new girl she doesn't like.

4. Mrs. Thurston hosts a secret share party–

    A. to help the students learn about each other.

    B. to celebrate the holiday season with presents.

    C. to celebrate the end of the school year.

    D. to make the students stop laughing at Britte.

5. What message is the author of this story most likely trying to communicate?

    A. Seventh-grade students can be cruel.

    B. Many people enjoy painting.

    C. Don't judge a book by its cover.

    D. Art supplies are expensive.

Go On ▶

       © Englefield & Associates, Inc.

Beyond Color

1   Mention the word "astronomer," and you will generally conjure an image of a person with a telescope. Whether it's an amateur astronomer using a small telescope in a back yard or a professional with an enormous version in an observatory, the idea of an astronomer typically goes hand in hand with this instrument that helps him or her magnify faraway objects.

2   Recent astronomers, however, have found that there is much more to the universe than that which can be seen with even the aided eye. In the 1980s, astronomers began to study space using an exciting development known as infrared radiation. Infrared radiation is heat given off by objects that is outside the range of wavelengths that humans see as colors. Some objects in space that are not visible to the eye because they are hidden by clouds of gas and dust, give off infrared waves that are able to pass through these barriers.

3   Using satellites, astronomers can put infrared telescopes into space to pick up some of the infrared radiation given off by objects in the universe. At certain wavelengths of infrared, the dust in space becomes almost transparent, and stars that are too small and cool to be seen through a telescope show up.

4   Stars are not the only objects that are easier to view using infrared; some galaxies, particle clouds, molecules, and even planets can be detected with infrared. If a planet or some other object in space is near a bright star, the brightness of the star will often make any objects around it difficult to see. In infrared wavelengths, however, the star's brightness is diminished, and the nearby object becomes easier to find.

5   For many objects in space, infrared astronomy is an important component of getting a more complete image. It is similar to adding specific details to a painting that only shows basic outlines. It also enables astronomers to find objects they would never otherwise be able to see. With many infrared projects planned for the future, it is likely that infrared will help astronomers learn much more about the universe we live in.

Go On

6. In paragraph 2 of the selection, why does the author include a description of how infrared works in the field of astronomy?

   A. so readers will understand how astronomers are using infrared to their advantage

   B. so readers will know that infrared is a tool only useful to astronomers

   C. so readers will understand that infrared has very little use in astronomy

   D. so readers will be aware that all satellites use infrared technology

7. Read this sentence from the first paragraph of the passage.

   "Mention the word 'astronomer,' and you will generally *conjure* an image of a person with a telescope."

   What does the word *conjure* mean?

   A. to build

   B. to connect pieces together

   C. to cause to appear

   D. to grow

Go On

8. Is using infrared technology in the field of astronomy a good idea?

    Provide **four** details from the selection to support your answer.

9. Using the information in the passage, what can you infer that scientists have found using infrared technology?

    A. spaceships

    B. the sun

    C. planets

    D. winds

10. What can you most likely predict after reading the passage "Beyond Color"?

    A. Scientists will discontinue the use of infrared technology because it is an unreliable way to find objects in space.

    B. Scientists will continue to use infrared technology because it gives scientists a more complete image of space.

    C. Infrared technology will not be used until scientists invent a way to harness its harmful radiation.

    D. Scientists will begin to use infrared technology to learn about planet Earth.

Go On ▶

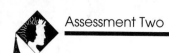

> **Read this selection. Then answer the questions that follow.**

Paula Finds a Treasure

1 *Paula Stringley thought she had found a treasure chest when she came across her Grandmother Ella's old trunk in the attic. Underneath her grandmother's photos, newspaper clippings, and her grandmother's college yearbook from Barnard, Paula came across a leather bound journal. As she leafed through it, her eyes landed on the following entry.*

2 May 15, 1921

3 Dear Diary,

4 Oh my dear. I am so confused, I don't even know where to begin. Father has increased the pressure for my decision. I know he means well by insisting that it is in my best interest to marry Phillip. In my mind, I know he may be right. Phillip is everything that I've ever dreamed of in a man.

5 He's kind and gentle, intelligent, fairly humorous, and he certainly has a good heart and good intentions. He comes from one of the most respected families in New York. He was educated at an Ivy League school, and he stands first in line to replace his father as president of Stringley Textiles. A future with him would certainly be secure, but in my heart, I cannot help but feel that fate is pushing me toward another path. Barnard is perhaps the most prestigious women's college in the country, and it is right here in the city. The fact that I have been accepted must be a sign that the road I travel will be different from what is expected of me. I can go and study to become an English teacher and write in my free time. Father says the only reason a woman must go to college at all is to find a husband, and because I have already done that, I have no need for further schooling.

6 Why must it be one or the other? Why can I not have my education and a marriage and family? Father believes the two are irreconcilable and that I must chose either the life of a schooled spinster or one of wife and mother. Today I suggested to Father that I accept

Go On ▶

                   © Englefield & Associates, Inc.

Phillip's proposal and commence studies at Barnard in September. Surely we will be engaged for at least a year, during which time I can attend classes. Then, when we marry, I can continue my studies, as the school is only a short trip from the Stringley home. Father says that the role of the wife of the future president of Stringley Textiles will be a full-time job and that there will be little time for studies. He says that there is no possible way I could do both. Mother says I should marry Phillip and put aside the silly notion of a college degree. How can one's desire to better oneself be considered a "silly notion"? Don't they understand that it's my heart's desire to become a writer? If I marry Phillip, then they need not worry about my stability or happiness, for I do truly love him. But I love to write as well.

7   Could Mother be right? Do I have a right to want more than other girls in my position? I certainly would have more than any girl could want by marrying Phillip and having my primary role be that of wife and mother. He can offer so much: a beautiful home, fine clothing, and a position in society. I suppose the real question I must answer is whether my desire for personal fulfillment is more important than my obedience to my parents.

8   "Ella"

Go On ▶

11. How does Ella's father's view contribute to the conflict in the journal entry?

    Include **two** details from the journal entry in your answer.

12. Based on the information in the selection, which conclusion can the reader draw about Ella?

    A. Ella followed her father's advice.

    B. Ella was convinced to give up her "silly notions."

    C. Ella was able to reconcile her heart and mind.

    D. Ella opted to attend college rather than marry Phillip.

13. What is the main idea of the journal entry?

    A. Fathers think that their daughters are incapable of making rational decisions about their futures.

    B. Ella was a trailblazer who opened many doors for women who desire an education, a marriage, and a family.

    C. Ella struggles to understand why she must choose one role over another when it seems that she can accomplish both.

    D. Paula Stringley learns an important lesson about her family history.

Go On

14. Read the sentence from paragraph 5 of the selection.

   "Barnard is perhaps the most *prestigious* women's college in the country, and it is right here in the city."

   What is the meaning of the word *prestigious* as it is used in the sentence above?

   A. friendly

   B. well-respected

   C. expensive

   D. moderate

15. Based on the information in the selection, what do you predict Paula will do now that she has read her grandmother's journal entry?

   A. Paula will throw the journal away.

   B. Paula will pack the journal back in the trunk.

   C. Paula will read more of the journal.

   D. Paula will decide to go to college.

Go On

Read this selection. Then answer the questions that follow.

What Can a Positive Attitude Do for You?

1   Have you ever heard the philosophy that a bad situation is only as bad as you make it out to be? Many scientists, philosophers, and regular people believe that a change in attitude can change a person's whole view on life. It's all in your state of mind!

2   For example, imagine that you are watching your favorite football team play on TV. They get creamed! The final score is 48 to 14! Now, you have two different ways to react to this situation. One: You can feel sad about the loss and become angry with your favorite team. You can let the negative thoughts consume your entire outlook on life and decide that life is unfair because your team lost. Two: You can feel a little disappointed about the loss, but remember that it's just a game and your team will win and lose more games in the future. Besides, the game was fun to watch. You can decide not to let the game make you upset and to enjoy the rest of your day despite the loss.

3   The second method is no doubt harder to achieve than the first method; however, the second method can make you happier. Ancient philosopher Epictetus once said, "It's not what happens to you, but how you react to it that matters." He believed in the power of a positive attitude. So did the First Lady of the United States of America: "I am still determined to be cheerful and happy, in whatever situation I may be; for I have also learned from experience that the greater part of our happiness or misery depends upon our dispositions, and not upon our circumstances," Martha Washington said.

4   A positive attitude can make even the bleakest situations feel like they aren't so bad. It allows people to bounce back from defeat and keep going after they have failed so many times that their goal seems unreachable.

5   Some of the world's most successful people failed many times before they achieved great success. Thomas Edison made more than 6,000 failed attempts before he invented the electric light bulb. R. H. Macy, the founder of Macy's Department Store, tried five different professions (whaler, gold miner, stockbroker, real estate broker, and retailer) before becoming successful with his seventh attempt as a retailer with Macy's in Manhattan. Just imagine what would have happened if these great men let a negative attitude stop them from reaching their goals!

Go On

© Englefield & Associates, Inc.

6   A positive attitude can make life changes if a person works to maintain it in all situations—good and bad. Anna Freud, famous psychologist Sigmund Freud's youngest daughter, had the following reflection about attitude: "I was always looking outside myself for strength and confidence, but it comes from within. It is there all the time." So, next time you feel defeated or discouraged, be optimistic and change your attitude. You never know what success a positive attitude may bring you.

Go On ▶

16. The author wrote this passage to—

   A. inform the reader about successful men who failed many times.

   B. describe the feelings of someone who has failed.

   C. persuade the reader to try to have a positive attitude.

   D. explain steps that teach the reader how to keep a positive attitude.

18. Read this sentence from the third paragraph of the passage.

   "It's not what happens to you, but how you react to it that matters."

   Who said this quote?

   A. Martha Washington

   B. the author

   C. Thomas Edison

   D. Epictetus

17. What is the essential message of this passage?

   A. You should never give up, even if you fail many times.

   B. You should try to maintain a positive attitude in all situations.

   C. You should not lie because it may hurt someone's feelings.

   D. You should not care if your favorite football team loses a game.

Go On

> **Read this selection. Then answer the questions that follow.**

Super Sam

1   "Lizzie! Lizzie! I'm Superhero! Watch me soar through the air!"

2   My little brother, Sam, goes through phases. Last month, he was in a "pretending to be a domesticated mammal" phase. He wanted our mom to put his dinner plate on the floor so he could eat like a canine, but she refused. Now, he's moved on to a superhero phase, and he wears this ridiculous red cape all the time. I think it used to be part of a Halloween costume.

3   "Not right now, Sam," I told him, waving him away without looking up from my algebra book. "I have a ton of homework to finish."

4   "Please, Lizzie? Just watch me once," he begged. "Then I'll go away." He began to run back and forth across my bedroom, arms stretched out to the sides, pretending to fly.

5   "No, Sam! Not now." I must have been talking louder than I thought, because he took a step in reverse. I lowered my voice. "I don't have time for your new persona. I have to finish my algebra so I can go set the table. You know if the table isn't set when Mom gets home, she'll be furious." Sam didn't say anything, but I could tell he was stomping with extra emphasis as he left my room.

6   I looked at my watch after Sam left: five o'clock. Mom would be home in fifteen minutes, and I had only completed a few tedious problems. Algebra was my worst subject, and I was supposed to finish the assignment first so Mom or Dad could review it after dinner. But today's homework was much more difficult than our usual assignments, and I was nowhere near completion.

7   Five minutes later, I was still stuck on the problem I had been grappling with when Sam first interrupted me. I put my pencil down and sighed, wondering how I would be able to finish everything in time. Just as I was picking up the pencil again, I heard a shattering noise coming from downstairs.

Go On ▶

8   Thoughts raced through my mind as I ran down the stairs. At first I figured that Sam had probably knocked something over while he was running around pretending to fly. But what if it was something else? What if someone had broken into our house? What if Sam was seriously injured?

9   "Sam?" I called his name as I looked in the front hallway, then in the living room. I was about to move on to the dining room when I heard someone whimpering quietly. The sound seemed to be coming from the kitchen, so I peeked my head through the doorway. Sam was on top of the counter, huddled beneath the cabinets. There was a broken plate on the floor.

10   I approached the edge of the counter. "Sam?" I asked gently, "What happened?"

11   Sam raised his head. "I was going to set the table," he said, sniffling, "but I couldn't reach the plates. So I got up here, and when I tried to climb down, I dropped it."

12   The plate had broken into six or seven large segments. I picked them up and put them in the wastebasket. Then I walked back over to the counter and put my hand on top of Sam's. I couldn't help but notice how small it was.

13   "Why were you trying to set the table, Sam? You know that's my job."

14   Sam looked up at me with his big round eyes. "You were working so hard, and I didn't want you to get in trouble. Besides," he said, his eyes becoming brighter, "Superhero can set the table with lightning speed!"

15   I chuckled and lowered him down off the countertop. "Tell you what, Superhero. How about we set the table together? I will get the plates and glasses, and you can do the silverware."

16   "Well . . ." he said doubtfully, "I guess Superhero could do the silverware."

17   "And after that," I said, "maybe you can fly for me." Sam's face lit up. He opened the drawer and started pulling out silverware as fast as he could. I smiled as he hurried to the table, his cape flapping behind him. Sometimes, he was a lot more super than I realized.

Go On ▶

19. What problem does Lizzie encounter early in the story?

    A. She has trouble with her math homework.

    B. Sam drops a plate.

    C. Sam won't set the table.

    D. Sam won't stop acting like a dog.

20. Why did the author write this story?

    A. to entertain readers

    B. to explain why children act like superheroes

    C. to tell the story of an unhappy little boy

    D. to inform readers about the difficulty of doing Algebra homework

21. Why does Sam want to set the table?

    A. to let Lizzie finish her homework

    B. to use his lightning speed

    C. to be able to climb on the counter

    D. to break the plates

22. What causes Lizzie to decide to play along with Sam's Superhero character?

    A. Sam breaks a plate and she wants him to clean it up.

    B. Sam tries to give Lizzie time to do her homework by attempting to set the table.

    C. Sam tells Lizzie he will lay out the silverware if she watches him fly.

    D. Sam won't stop crying until Lizzie plays along.

Go On ▶

Read this selection. Then answer the questions that follow.

Sheba

1   Growing up, my brother and I used to play in the woods behind our house. At night, we were frightened by the rustling and howling noises that came from there. During the day, though, we would play hide-and-seek with other children from the neighborhood. My beloved hiding spot was under a fallen oak tree. The trunk had cracked at the base, and when it fell, it brought down a neighboring oak. These fallen trunks were tangled together, and the intertwined branches, with their leafy tops, formed the perfect child-sized shelter. I would nestle below the natural canopy when I hid, pulling my knees to my chest and watching vigilantly for the seeker. We played many rounds of the adventurous game before I was discovered in my special hiding locale.

2   Other times, we would just wander around by ourselves. We discovered a variety of activities to entertain ourselves. We constantly had to be careful not to trip over tree roots or rocks that protruded from the ground. One of my earliest memories is of standing with my brother, trying to unbury a large rock that was embedded in the soil. We tried to free the boulder-like fixture with crude tools, sticks, and smaller rocks. Needless to say, we were unsuccessful. Despite its simplicity, the activity was enjoyable. That was the kind of adventure we found in our private forest.

3   I will never forget our special scavenger hunts. These weren't your ordinary scavenger hunts, but ones that made me feel like a real detective. My brother and I would take turns finding "clues" in the woods. Sometimes the clues could be as simple as the footprint of a rabbit. We would follow the tracks and make up fantastical stories about where the rabbit was going, why it was heading in a certain direction, and the dangers it may have encountered along the way. One time we picked up on the tracks of what appeared to be a large bobcat. It would have been unusual for a bobcat to wander up so close to a neighborhood, but we had heard stories about such an incident. I remember the thrill I felt as we followed the deep imprints up to a particularly large oak tree. Much to our surprise and disappointment, it wasn't a bobcat after all. The tracks turned out to be those of Old Man Smith's hound.

4   Those adventures could keep us occupied for hours. We never worried about finding something to do on a summer day or on the weekend. Our "investigations" were over when the clues went cold or we grew tired of playing.

5   As I reflect on the time I spent in the woods, I am pleasantly reminded of another gem it held for my family. One hazy, hot August afternoon found us brothers seeking out snakes, turtles, and crayfish near the trickling brook that flowed through the middle of the woods. Nothing cold-blooded was to

Go On▶

be found that day; instead, an ugly puppy greeted us. Her dark black fur was muddy and matted, and she was unrecognizable as any particular breed of dog.

6   The little animal cowered in the special hiding spot I used when I played hide-and-seek. When I stretched out my hand, she crawled out. She sniffed my hand and arm, then licked me. It was as if we were old friends. She was friendly and gentle, but her ragged appearance made us wonder if she was healthy. We were surprised to see her, but happy to have her as our companion.

7   The dog followed us to our house that day. We could tell right away that Mom wasn't entirely sweet on the idea of taking in a stray dog for a pet. My brother and I promised Mom that she would never have to remind us to feed our new canine friend. We agreed to do extra chores around the house as payment for the dog food we would need. Finally, we convinced her to let us keep the dog after the veterinarian examined her and told us she would make a fine pet. We named her Sheba, and she has been a loyal member of our family since I was seven. I am grateful that she hid in my spot until I found her. She is one of the many natural wonders my brother and I found in the woods.

Go On

23. What kind of relationship do the narrator and the narrator's brother have?

   A. a violent one

   B. a strained one

   C. a friendly one

   D. a bitter one

24. In the first paragraph of the passage, which of the following best describes the mood created by the narrator's description of the hiding place?

   A. The narrator reflects on a place the narrator found to be serene, secret, and safe.

   B. The narrator reflects on a place the narrator found to be scary and insecure.

   C. The narrator reflects on a place the narrator found to be secret and peaceful, but unstable.

   D. The narrator reflects on a place the narrator found to be cramped and unstable, but secret.

25. What point of view does the author use and why does he use this point of view?

   A. The author uses third person because he is telling a story about his brother and the dog.

   B. The author uses first person because he argues that Sheba is a great dog despite its ugly appearance.

   C. The author uses third person because he is telling a fictional story.

   D. The author uses first person because he is telling a story about his own life.

26. The story is organized by—

   A. providing a chronological account of Sheba's life.

   B. describing childhood memories of the narrator.

   C. providing details on caring for a pet.

   D. discussing the events of one day in the life of the brothers.

Go On ▶

27. A theme found throughout this story is about—

    A. neighborhood friendships.

    B. past memories.

    C. family traditions.

    D. man's best friend.

28. Why are paragraphs 6 and 7 important to this story?

    A. They describe what the dog looked like.

    B. They tell what kind of family the boys had.

    C. They provide details about the boys' adventure in the woods.

    D. They explain how Sheba becomes a member of the family.

29. Read the sentence from paragraph 5 of the story.

"As I reflect on the time I spent in the woods, I am pleasantly reminded of *another gem it held for my family*."

The author uses the phrase *another gem it held for my family* to describe—

    A. a valuable gem that the brothers found in the woods.

    B. the stray dog the brothers found that became part of their family.

    C. the author's special hiding spot.

    D. the author's memories of playing hide-and-seek.

Go On ▶

> **Read this selection. Then answer the questions that follow.**

Clean Machines

1   Lift the hoods of 99.99% of the automobiles on the road today, and you will find internal combustion engines. These engines depend on irreplaceable fossil fuels and create emissions that pollute. Emissions contribute to the depletion of the ozone layer and to the greenhouse effect. As more and more cars are demanded around the world, the environmental effects are bound to expand.

2   Enter California. An estimated 95% of Californians live in areas that do not meet federally required clean air standards because of a high amount of emissions. Most people blame the poor air condition on cars and trucks. Based on these dismal figures, legislators decided to act. They passed a law stating that by 2003, 10% of cars sold in California must be non-polluting; despite good intentions, this law was modified, allowing for more leniency. Regardless, the fact that people are asking for lower emissions has forced auto manufacturers to act.

3   Electric cars are the most obvious answer to the non-polluting, non-emissions standard. Since the fuel crisis of the 1970s, auto manufacturers have increased their experiments with battery-powered cars; however, these have many drawbacks. After fewer than 100 miles, the batteries must be recharged. This can take as long as eight hours. The batteries are very heavy; they can double the weight of the car. Finally, the batteries are extremely expensive and need to be replaced every three to four years. All these factors have contributed to the belief that battery-driven electric cars are not very practical.

4   However, new technology on the horizon will hopefully make electric cars more appealing. The answer to the battery problem appears to be the fuel cell. A fuel cell is not a battery that stores an electrical charge. Instead, it creates electricity on the move using hydrogen, with the only byproduct being water. Thus, it does not need to be plugged in to recharge and is lighter than traditional batteries.

Go On▶

5   Fuel cell technology has been improved and may become an option, but the fuel itself presents a problem. Gasoline and methanol are the fuels of choice right now, since the technology for using hydrogen is still primitive. The gasoline or methanol is refined in an on-board processor to extract hydrogen. This method still creates some emissions, but not nearly the amount created by a traditional internal combustion engine. There are some problems, however. Gasoline is the fossil fuel we are trying to avoid using in the first place, and methanol is highly toxic. Also, the process that changes gasoline or methanol to hydrogen is difficult. Using pure hydrogen is the best alternative, since the only emissions it would create would be water and heat. However, it is difficult to compress enough hydrogen to make a car go very far, and hydrogen is extremely flammable. Researchers are working on the technology. Until they come up with a safe and efficient method, gasoline and methanol appear to be the only options.

6   Independent carmakers are rushing to develop the best technology for electric cars. Amory Lovins of the Rocky Mountain Institute is working on a car made completely of plastics. Major auto manufacturers are also dedicating teams of engineers to working on fuel cell cars. They see this as the car of the future. It will not depend on fossil fuels and will not contribute to the greenhouse effect. It will be a car with no negative environmental impact whatsoever.

Go On

Mix and Match

6   Carmakers and consumers are discovering that sometimes, finding the solution to a problem does not mean throwing an idea out altogether, but revising it. In the wake of new demands for nonpolluting automobiles, manufacturers have come up with a compromise in the form of the hybrid car.

7   Electric cars have appeared to be the ideal solution to the gas guzzling, polluting cars with internal combustion engines. However, electric cars have problems, including the limited distance they can travel and the weight and expense of batteries. Hybrid cars solve these problems while also dramatically cutting down on polluting emissions.

9   These cars are called hybrids because they mix and match technology, using a combination of energy sources. They use both an internal combustion engine and a small set of batteries. The batteries are less expensive and lighter than those found in purely electric cars. Unlike older versions of electric cars, which ran on huge batteries, hybrids do not need to be plugged in to recharge. Instead, they use the excess power from the gas engine to charge the batteries.

10   Hybrids combine the best of both gasoline and electric-powered worlds. Gasoline engines are most efficient for driving long distances at faster speeds, but they waste a great deal of fuel, especially when the car starts and when it runs while not moving. Electric motors, on the other hand, are efficient when starting up and do not pollute while the car is standing still; however, in highway driving, their batteries run down quickly. A hybrid uses the electric motor to start the car and to accelerate. Once the car gets going, the gasoline engine kicks in. While driving, the hybrid uses the excess power from the engine to recharge the batteries.

11   Makers of hybrids report fuel economy of up to 70 miles per gallon. This is more than twice as efficient as most compact cars with internal combustion engines, which means half the emissions. Not a bad compromise.

Go On

30. How do hybrid cars compare to electric cars?

    A. both use fuel cell technology

    B. both use lightweight batteries

    C. both offer cleaner environmental technologies

    D. both rely solely on fossil fuels

31. What is a similar idea presented by the authors in these two selections?

    A. An alternative to today's traditional automobile will never be found.

    B. An alternative to today's traditional automobile is only in the development stage.

    C. An alternative to today's traditional automobile has been developed, but more work needs to be done to make it more effective.

    D. An alternative to today's traditional automobile is unnecessary.

Go On

32. What is the purpose of these two selections?

   A. to entertain the reader

   B. to inform the reader

   C. to worry the reader

   D. to anger the reader

33. What problem does the fuel cell introduce?

   A. It is extremely heavy.

   B. It needs to be plugged in to be recharged.

   C. The fuel that would work best is difficult to compress.

   D. Its emissions are greater than the internal combustion engine.

34. In the context of these articles, what is the best definition of hybrid?

   A. something that gives up its good qualities for the good qualities of another

   B. something having two kinds of components that work together to produce a common result

   C. something that replaces another item of the same kind

   D. something that is a pure breed

35. According to the first selection, "Clean Cars," why should car manufacturers make electric cars?

   A. to provide cars that create more emissions

   B. to provide cars that sit at dealerships

   C. to provide cars that meet increasing consumer demand

   D. to provide cars with heavy batteries

Go On

36. Why are electric cars seen as the ideal replacement for cars with internal combustion engines?

    A. Electric cars do not pollute the air.

    B. Electric cars are simpler to make.

    C. Electric cars are already widely available.

    D. Electric cars can travel for long distances.

38. What kind of engine do most cars have today?

    A. electric

    B. hybrid

    C. internal combustion

    D. fuel cell

37. Which of the following best describes what could happen if electric or hybrid cars aren't manufactured?

    A. batteries will become heavier

    B. batteries will never be needed

    C. pollution from cars will continue to deplete the ozone layer

    D. California lawmakers will pass more clean air laws

Go On

39. What is the main idea of the third paragraph of "Clean Machines"?

    A. Electric cars solved the pollution problem with automobiles.

    B. More states are regulating the amount of emissions that cars produce.

    C. Electric cars must be recharged after less than 100 miles.

    D. Electric cars are non-polluting, but they are not very practical.

40. The word *non-polluting* means–

    A. clean.

    B. clear.

    C. dirty.

    D. fake.

1 Ⓐ Ⓑ Ⓒ Ⓓ

2 Ⓐ Ⓑ Ⓒ Ⓓ

3 Ⓐ Ⓑ Ⓒ Ⓓ

4 Ⓐ Ⓑ Ⓒ Ⓓ

5 Ⓐ Ⓑ Ⓒ Ⓓ

6 Ⓐ Ⓑ Ⓒ Ⓓ

7 Ⓐ Ⓑ Ⓒ Ⓓ

8

9 Ⓐ Ⓑ Ⓒ Ⓓ

10 Ⓐ Ⓑ Ⓒ Ⓓ

11

12 Ⓐ Ⓑ Ⓒ Ⓓ

13 Ⓐ Ⓑ Ⓒ Ⓓ

14 Ⓐ Ⓑ Ⓒ Ⓓ

15 Ⓐ Ⓑ Ⓒ Ⓓ

16 Ⓐ Ⓑ Ⓒ Ⓓ

17 Ⓐ Ⓑ Ⓒ Ⓓ

18 Ⓐ Ⓑ Ⓒ Ⓓ

19 Ⓐ Ⓑ Ⓒ Ⓓ

20 Ⓐ Ⓑ Ⓒ Ⓓ

21 Ⓐ Ⓑ Ⓒ Ⓓ

22 Ⓐ Ⓑ Ⓒ Ⓓ

23 Ⓐ Ⓑ Ⓒ Ⓓ

24 Ⓐ Ⓑ Ⓒ Ⓓ

25 Ⓐ Ⓑ Ⓒ Ⓓ

26 Ⓐ Ⓑ Ⓒ Ⓓ

27 Ⓐ Ⓑ Ⓒ Ⓓ

28 Ⓐ Ⓑ Ⓒ Ⓓ

29 Ⓐ Ⓑ Ⓒ Ⓓ

30 Ⓐ Ⓑ Ⓒ Ⓓ

31 Ⓐ Ⓑ Ⓒ Ⓓ

32 Ⓐ Ⓑ Ⓒ Ⓓ

33 Ⓐ Ⓑ Ⓒ Ⓓ

34 Ⓐ Ⓑ Ⓒ Ⓓ

35 Ⓐ Ⓑ Ⓒ Ⓓ

36 Ⓐ Ⓑ Ⓒ Ⓓ

37 Ⓐ Ⓑ Ⓒ Ⓓ

38 Ⓐ Ⓑ Ⓒ Ⓓ

39 Ⓐ Ⓑ Ⓒ Ⓓ

40 Ⓐ Ⓑ Ⓒ Ⓓ

Notes

Notes

Notes

Copying is Prohibited

Show What You Know® on the COMMON CORE

Assessing Student Knowledge of the Common Core State Standards (CCSS)
Reading • Mathematics • Grades 3–8

Diagnostic Test-Preparation Student Workbooks and Parent/Teacher Editions for Grades 3–5

Single Subject Student Workbooks and Parent/Teacher Editions for Grades 6–8

For more information, call our toll-free number: 1.877.PASSING (727.7464)
or visit our website: www.showwhatyouknowpublishing.com